Mc
Graw
Hill

Cover and Title Page: Nathan Love

www.mheonline.com/readingwonders

Send all inquiries to:
McGraw-Hill Education
2 Penn Plaza
New York, NY 10121

ISBN: 978-0-02-131548-2
MHID: 0-02-131548-5

Printed in the United States of America

8 9 10 11 12 LMN 23 22 21 20

E

California

Wonders

ELD
Companion Worktext

Program Authors

Diane August

Jana Echevarria

Josefina V. Tinajero

Mc
Graw
Hill

Unit 1

Growing and Learning

The Big Idea

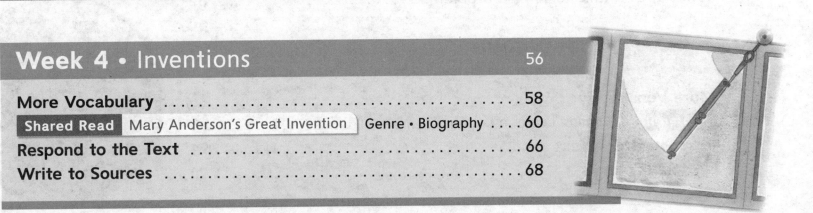

Unit 2

Figure It Out

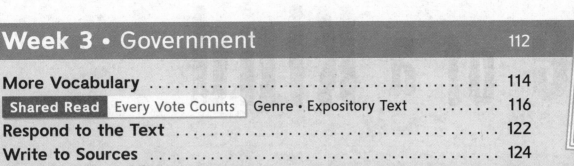

Unit 3

One of a Kind

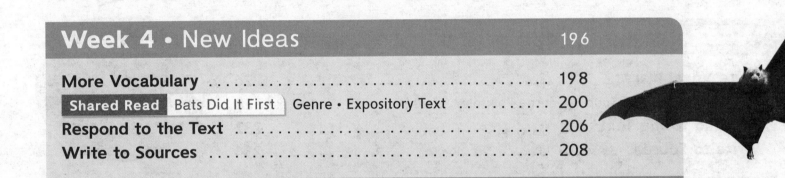

Meet the Challenge

The Big Idea

TAKE ACTION

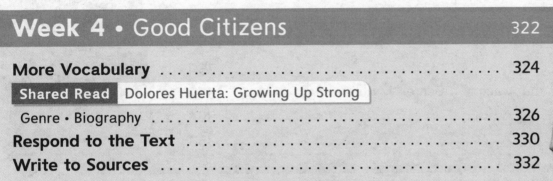

Think It Over

The Big Idea

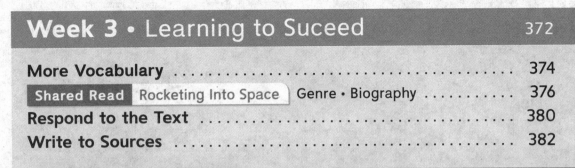

(t) NASA (c) Richard Ellis/Getty Images News/Getty Images (b) Daryll Collins

Unit 1

Growing and Learning

The Big Idea

How can learning help us grow?

14

COLLABORATE

What is the girl doing? Why is she laughing? What can she learn from stories. Write words about stories in the web.

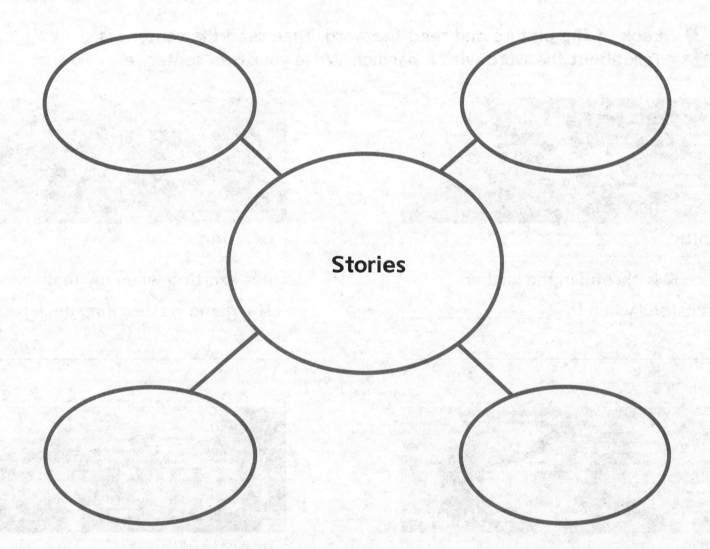

Stories

Discuss why the girl is reading the book. Use the words from the web. You can say:

The girl is reading because _____.

She is happy because _____.

ELD.PI.3.1.Ex, ELD.PI.3.1.Br, ELD.PI.3.5.Ex, ELD.PI.3.5.Br, ELD.PI.3.12.Ex, ELD.PI.3.12.Br See the California Standards section.

15

Look at the picture and read the word. Then read the sentences. Talk about the word with a partner. Write your own sentence.

careful

The cook is **careful** in the kitchen.

I am *careful* when I _____

_____.

exciting

It is **exciting** when my team wins.

The game was *exciting* because _____

_____.

escape

The dog **escapes** his owner.

Dogs *escape* because _____

_____.

important

The White House is an **important** building.

The White House is *important* because

_____.

knowledge

We have **knowledge** about our planet.

I have *knowledge* about _____

_____ .

perfect

Sue makes a **perfect** sandwich.

I have a *perfect* _____

_____ .

Words and Phrases
Homophones

too = **very**
I am <u>too</u> warm.

to = **in the direction of**
We are going <u>to</u> the library.

Read the sentences below. Write the homophone that means the same as the underlined word or words.

We are going <u>in the direction</u> of the store.

We are going _____ the store.

Slow down because you are going <u>very</u> fast.

Slow down because you are going _____ fast.

>> *Go Digital* **Add these homophones to your New Words notebook. Write a sentence to show the meaning of each homophone.**

COLLABORATE

1 Talk About It

Read the title. Discuss what you see. Write your ideas.

What does the title tell you?

_____

_____

_____

_____

What does the illustration show?

_____

_____

_____

_____

Take notes as you read the text.

BRUNO'S NEW HOME

Essential Question

? **What can stories teach you?**

Read how one story taught a bear an important lesson.

ELD.PI.3.1.Ex, ELD.PI.3.1.Br See the California Standards section.

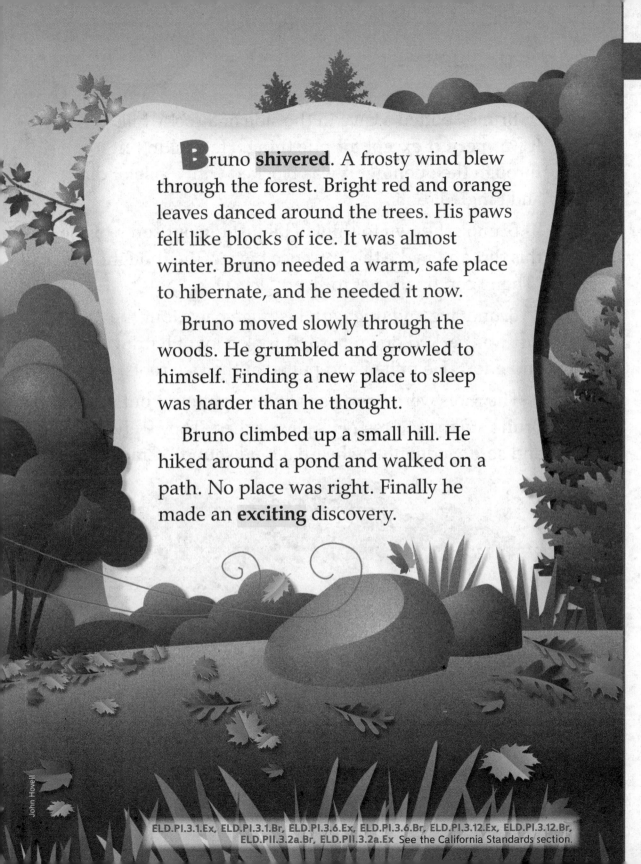

Bruno **shivered**. A frosty wind blew through the forest. Bright red and orange leaves danced around the trees. His paws felt like blocks of ice. It was almost winter. Bruno needed a warm, safe place to hibernate, and he needed it now.

Bruno moved slowly through the woods. He grumbled and growled to himself. Finding a new place to sleep was harder than he thought.

Bruno climbed up a small hill. He hiked around a pond and walked on a path. No place was right. Finally he made an **exciting** discovery.

John Howell

Text Evidence

① Specific Vocabulary Ⓐ Ⓒ Ⓣ

The word *shiver* means "to shake from cold." Underline the words that tell why Bruno shivered.

② Sentence Structure Ⓐ Ⓒ Ⓣ

Reread the last sentence in the first paragraph. Draw a box around the pronoun *he*. Write the noun that *he* refers to.

_____

What does Bruno need right now? Circle the words that tell you.

③ Comprehension

Character

Reread the second paragraph. What details help you figure out how Bruno feels? Underline the details. How does Bruno feel about finding a place to sleep?

_____

ELD.PI.3.1.Ex, ELD.PI.3.1.Br, ELD.PI.3.6.Ex, ELD.PI.3.6.Br, ELD.PI.3.12.Ex, ELD.PI.3.12.Br, ELD.PII.3.2a.Br, ELD.PII.3.2a.Ex See the California Standards section.

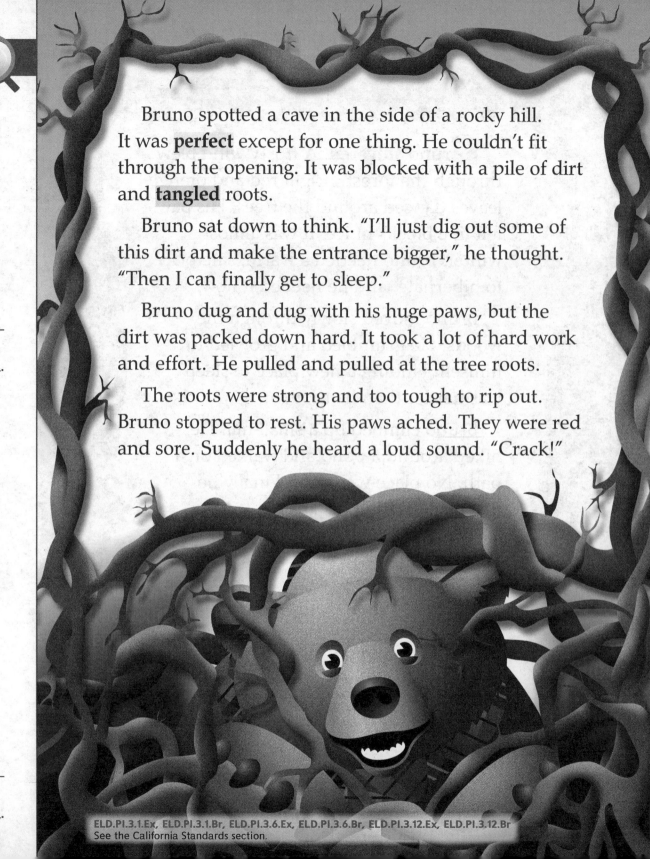

Text Evidence

1 Specific Vocabulary Ⓐ Ⓒ Ⓣ

Look at the word *tangled*. Then look at the picture. The word *tangled* means "twisted together." Why are the tangled roots a problem for Bruno?

_____

_____.

2 Sentence Structure Ⓐ Ⓒ Ⓣ

Reread the second paragraph. Circle the punctuation marks that show someone is thinking. Underline the words that show who is thinking.

COLLABORATE

3 Talk About It

Explain how Bruno tries to makes the entrance bigger. Then write about it.

_____

_____.

Bruno spotted a cave in the side of a rocky hill. It was **perfect** except for one thing. He couldn't fit through the opening. It was blocked with a pile of dirt and **tangled** roots.

Bruno sat down to think. "I'll just dig out some of this dirt and make the entrance bigger," he thought. "Then I can finally get to sleep."

Bruno dug and dug with his huge paws, but the dirt was packed down hard. It took a lot of hard work and effort. He pulled and pulled at the tree roots.

The roots were strong and too tough to rip out. Bruno stopped to rest. His paws ached. They were red and sore. Suddenly he heard a loud sound. "Crack!"

ELD.PI.3.1.Ex, ELD.PI.3.1.Br, ELD.PI.3.6.Ex, ELD.PI.3.6.Br, ELD.PI.3.12.Ex, ELD.PI.3.12.Br
See the California Standards section.

Bruno turned quickly and saw a small squirrel eating a nut. He stopped eating and smiled at Bruno.

"You look like you need help," said the squirrel.

Bruno sighed. "I have been trying to fit into this cave, but it's **hopeless**. I've been digging and digging, but I haven't improved the opening at all."

"I'm Jack, and I can help," said the squirrel.

"But you are too small," said Bruno.

Jack told Bruno to sit down and rest. Bruno sat and yawned as Jack scampered away. A few minutes later, he came back.

John Hovell

ELD.PI.3.1.Ex, ELD.PI.3.1.Br, ELD.PI.3.6.Ex, ELD.PI.3.6.Br, ELD.PI.3.12.Ex, ELD.PI.3.12.Br
See the California Standards section.

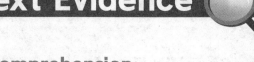
1 Comprehension

Character

Reread the first and second paragraphs. Circle the words that show the squirrel is friendly. Underline the words that show the squirrel is helpful.

2 Specific Vocabulary ACT

The word *hopeless* means "no hope." Underline the sentence that tells why Bruno feels hopeless.

COLLABORATE

3 Talk About It

How does Bruno feel about Jack? Write your ideas. Cite text evidence.

_____

_____

_____

_____

1 Specific Vocabulary Ⓐ C T

Reread the last sentence of the second paragraph. To *pay attention* means "watch closely." Underline the words in the second sentence that tell what "paid attention" means.

2 Sentence Structure Ⓐ C T

Adjectives describe people, places, and objects. Reread the second paragraph. Circle the adjectives that describe the spot Bruno moved to.

COLLABORATE

3 Talk About It

How are the lion and mouse in Bruno's book like Bruno and Jack?

Justify your answer. _____

_____

_____ .

"What you need is a book," said Jack. "Reading can help you become educated. Books are filled with **knowledge**." He handed Bruno a thick red book.

Bruno moved to a bright, sunny spot. He put on his glasses and tried to concentrate on the story. He **paid careful attention** to the plot.

The story was about a lion and a mouse. The lion thought the mouse was too small to help him. One day the lion got caught in a net. The mouse chewed the net's ropes and helped the lion **escape**.

ELD.PI.3.1.Ex, ELD.PI.3.1.Br, ELD.PI.3.6.Ex, ELD.PI.3.6.Br, ELD.PI.3.7.Ex, ELD.PI.3.7.Br, ELD.PI.3.12.Ex, ELD.PI.3.12.Br See the California Standards section.

"Well, the lion in this story learned an **important** lesson," said Bruno. "I think I did, too."

The story inspired Bruno. The mouse had sharp teeth, and so did Jack. Jack could help.

The new friends made a fine team. Jack chewed through the thick roots, and Bruno dug out the dirt. They worked together all afternoon. Finally, Bruno could fit through the opening.

"Are you satisfied and happy with your cozy new home?" asked Jack.

"I sure am!" said Bruno. "And I learned something, too. Good friends come in small packages."

Make Connections

? Talk about the story of the lion and the mouse. How did it help Bruno solve his problem? **ESSENTIAL QUESTION**

Discuss how you and your friends help one another. **TEXT TO SELF**

ELD.PI.3.1.Ex, ELD.PI.3.1.Br, ELD.PI.3.6.Ex, ELD.PI.3.6.Br, ELD.PI.3.11.Ex, ELD.PI.3.11.Br, ELD.PII.3.6.Ex, ELD.PII.3.6.Br See the California Standards section.

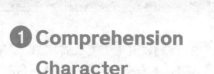

Text Evidence

1 Comprehension

Character

A trait is what makes someone or something special. Read the second paragraph. Underline the words that describe Jack's special trait.

2 Sentence Structure Ⓐ Ⓒ Ⓣ

Reread the second sentence in the third paragraph. Circle the word that connects Jack and Bruno's actions. Underline the actions.

COLLABORATE

3 Talk About It

Bruno says, "Good friends come in small packages." What does Bruno mean? Do you agree with Bruno?

Justify your answer. _____

_____

_____.

Respond to the Text

Partner Discussion Work with a partner. Answer the questions. Discuss what you learned about "Bruno's New Home." Write the page numbers where you found text evidence.

What is Bruno's problem?

Text Evidence 🔍

I read that Bruno is cold because _____.

Page(s): _____

In the story, the problem with the cave is _____.

Page(s): _____

According to the story, Bruno needs help to make the

entrance bigger because _____.

Page(s): _____

How does the book inspire Bruno?

Text Evidence 🔍

The story that Bruno reads is about _____.

Page(s): _____

Jack is like the mouse because _____.

Page(s): _____

According to the story, the book teaches Bruno that _____.

Page(s): _____

Group Discussion Present your answers to the group. Cite text evidence to justify your thinking. Listen to and discuss the group's opinions about your answers.

 ELD.PI.3.1.Ex, ELD.PI.3.1.Br, ELD.PI.3.3.Ex, ELD.PI.3.3.Br, ELD.PI.3.6.Ex, ELD.PI.3.6.Br, ELD.PII.3.6.Ex, ELD.PII.3.6.Br See the California Standards section.

COLLABORATE

Write Work with a partner. Look at your notes about "Bruno's New Home." Then write your answer to the Essential Question. Use text evidence to support your answer. Use vocabulary words from this week's reading in your writing.

What does the story teach Bruno?

In the beginning of the story, Bruno needs _____

_____.

Jack wants _____, but Bruno thinks _____.

Jack gives Bruno a book about _____.

The book teaches Bruno that _____.

COLLABORATE

Share Writing Present your writing to the class. Discuss their opinions. Think about what the class has to say. Did they justify their claims? Explain why you agree or disagree with their claims. You can say:

I agree with _____.

That's a good comment, but _____.

Write to Sources

pages 18–23

Take Notes About the Text I took notes about the story on this chart. I will respond to the prompt: *Write a descriptive paragraph. Add to the story. Describe how Bruno thanks Jack. Tell why Jack is a good friend.*

Alicia

Bruno finds a cave, but roots block the opening.

↓

Bruno cannot pull out the roots.

↓

Jack chews through the roots.

↓

Bruno is happy with his new home.

ELD.PI.3.6.Ex, ELD.PI.3.6.Br See the California Standards section.

Write About the Text I used my notes to write a paragraph. It tells how Bruno thanks Jack.

Jack helped Bruno. Bruno wanted to thank Jack. Bruno gave Jack some delicious brown nuts. Jack smiled. Jack ate the nuts.

Bruno said, "Jack, you are a good friend. You chewed through the roots. You helped me fix my new home. Thank you."

TALK ABOUT IT

Text Evidence
Circle the words that come from the notes. Why does Alicia tell about this event?

Grammar
Underline the adjectives in the third sentence. Why did Alicia use adjectives?

Condense Ideas
Draw a box around the sentences that tell what Jack does. How can you condense the sentences with the word *and*?

Your Turn

Add a paragraph to the end of the story. Describe Bruno's new home.

>> Go Digital
Write your response online. Use your editing checklist.

TALK ABOUT IT

? **Essential Question**
What can traditions teach
you about cultures?

>> *Go Digital*

COLLABORATE

What is the woman in the photograph wearing? What is she doing? Write about her traditions in the web.

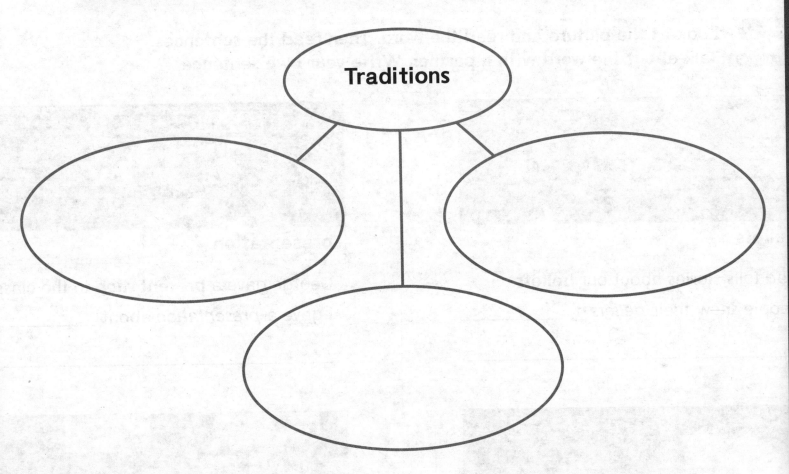

Traditions

Discuss what the woman is doing. How is she sharing her traditions? Use the words from the web. You can say:

_____ is sharing traditions by _____.

She shares traditions because _____

_____.

ELD.PI.3.1.Ex, ELD.PI.3.1.Br, ELD.PI.3.5.Ex, ELD.PI.3.5.Br, ELD.PI.3.12.Ex, ELD.PI.3.12.Br See the California Standards section.

29

More Vocabulary

COLLABORATE

Look at the picture and read the word. Then read the sentences. Talk about the word with a partner. Write your own sentence.

beliefs

Dad tells stories about our **beliefs**.

People show their *beliefs* by _____

_____.

presentation

George gave a **presentation** to the class.

I gave a *presentation* about _____

_____.

nervous

May is **nervous** on her first day of school.

I feel *nervous* when _____

_____.

pride

Max takes **pride** in his drawing.

I feel *pride* when I _____

_____.

share

Jack will **share** facts about his pet fish.

I like to *share* _____

_____ .

strength

They need **strength** to lift the sofa.

A person with *strength* is _____

_____ .

Words and Phrases
have and *have to*

have = **to own**
I <u>have</u> three books.

have to = must do something
I <u>have to</u> go to the store.

Read the sentences below. Look at the underlined words. Circle the words with the same meaning.

I <u>own</u> a new bike.

have   have to

Sam and Dad <u>must</u> paint the house.

have   have to

>> *Go Digital* Add *have* and *have to* to your New Words notebook. Write a sentence to show the meaning of each.

ELD.PI.3.1.Ex, ELD.PI.3.1.Br, ELD.PI.3.5.Ex, ELD.PI.3.5.Br, ELD.PI.3.12.Ex, ELD.PI.3.12.Br See the California Standards section.

COLLABORATE

1 Talk About It

Read the title. Look at the illustration. Discuss what you see. Write your ideas.

What is a dream catcher? What does it do?

_____

_____

_____

Who are the characters? What are they doing?

_____

_____

_____

Take notes as you read the text.

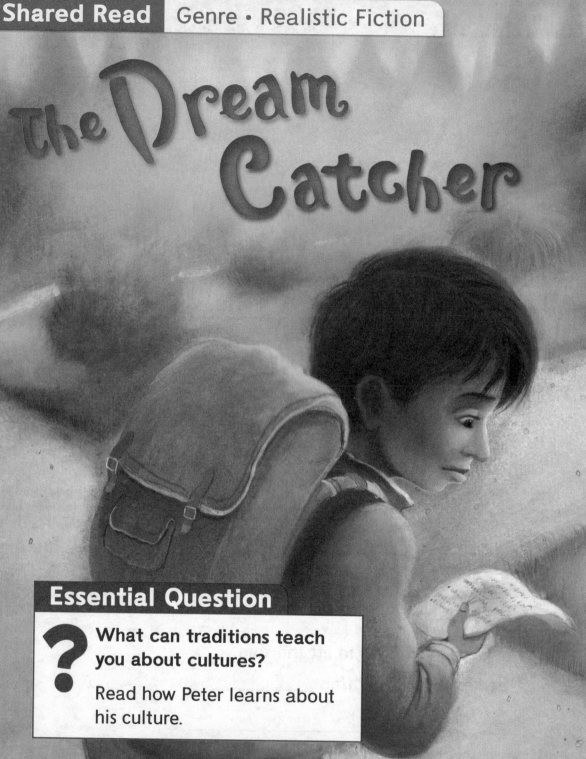

The Dream Catcher

Essential Question

? What can traditions teach you about cultures?

Read how Peter learns about his culture.

ELD.PI.3.1.Ex, ELD.PI.3.1.Br See the California Standards section.

Text Evidence

1 **Sentence Structure** A C T

Look at the first paragraph. Circle all the pronouns that refer to Peter. Then write them.

_____

2 **Specific Vocabulary** A C T

Reread the fourth paragraph. When Nokomis nods, she moves her head up and down. Why does Nokomis nod?

_____

3 **Comprehension**

At the beginning of the story, Peter is crying. Reread the third paragraph. Underline the sentence that tells why Peter is crying.

Peter walked home from school. Salty tears ran down his cheeks, and his stomach hurt. He didn't know what to do. Grandmother was waiting for him on the front porch.

"What's wrong, Biyen?" said Peter's grandmother. Biyen was the Ojibwe name for Peter. He called her Nokomis, which means grandmother.

Peter looked up. "I have to give a **presentation** where I talk about a family tradition. I know we have lots of **beliefs** and customs. Can you remind me of one?"

Nokomis smiled and **nodded** her head.

"Come with me," she said.

Richard Johnson

ELD.PI.3.6.Ex, ELD.PI.3.6.Br, ELD.PI.3.7.Ex, ELD.PI.3.7.Br, ELD.PII.3.1.Ex, ELD.PII.3.1.Br, ELD.PII.3.2a.Ex, ELD.PII.3.2a.Br See the California Standards section.

33

Text Evidence

1 Sentence Structure A C T

Look at the second sentence in the first paragraph. Underline the pronoun. Write the name of the person that the pronoun refers to.

_____

2 Specific Vocabulary A C T

Reread the third paragraph. The word *woven* means "crossing over and under." Underline the words that tell what woven string looks like.

COLLABORATE

3 Talk About It

Discuss how Peter feels after he opens the box. Underline the words that tell you. Talk about how Peter's feelings changed.

Peter followed Nokomis. She went to a closet and stretched to reach the top shelf. She pulled out a small box and blew away the dust. She handed it to Peter.

"Open it," she said.

Peter opened the box. He spotted a wooden hoop inside. It was in the shape of a circle. String was **woven** and twisted around the hoop. It looked like a spider web. A black bead sat near the center. Feathers hung from the bottom.

Peter wiped away his tears and smiled.

ELD.PI.3.6.Ex, ELD.PI.3.6.Br, ELD.PI.3.7.Ex, ELD.PI.3.7.Br, ELD.PI.3.12.Ex, ELD.PI.3.12.Br, ELD.PII.3.1.Ex, ELD.PII.3.1.Br, ELD.PII.3.2a.Ex, ELD.PII.3.2a.Br See the California Standards section.

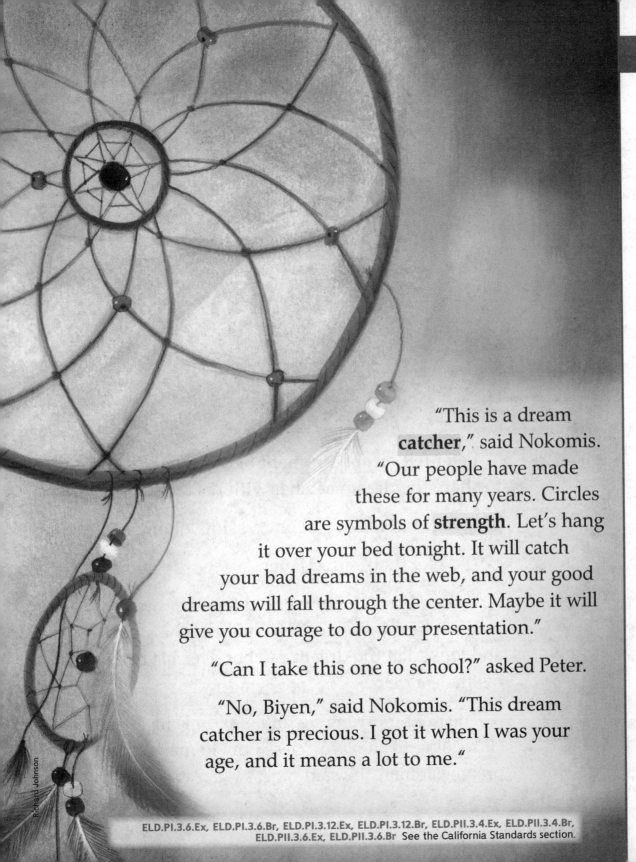

"This is a dream **catcher**," said Nokomis. "Our people have made these for many years. Circles are symbols of **strength**. Let's hang it over your bed tonight. It will catch your bad dreams in the web, and your good dreams will fall through the center. Maybe it will give you courage to do your presentation."

"Can I take this one to school?" asked Peter.

"No, Biyen," said Nokomis. "This dream catcher is precious. I got it when I was your age, and it means a lot to me."

Richard Johnson

ELD.PI.3.6.Ex, ELD.PI.3.6.Br, ELD.PI.3.12.Ex, ELD.PI.3.12.Br, ELD.PII.3.4.Ex, ELD.PII.3.4.Br, ELD.PII.3.6.Ex, ELD.PII.3.6.Br See the California Standards section.

Text Evidence

1 **Specific Vocabulary** Ⓐ Ⓒ Ⓣ

Adding *-er* to a word changes the word's meaning. *-er* means "a person or thing that does something." Look at the first sentence. Circle the word that ends in *-er*. Write what this word means.

_____

2 **Sentence Structure** Ⓐ Ⓒ Ⓣ

Look at the fifth sentence. This sentence has two parts. Circle the word that connects the two parts. Then underline the two actions.

COLLABORATE

3 **Talk About It**

Nokomis does not want Peter to bring the dream catcher to school. Discuss why. Write the words that tell you.

_____

35

1 **Specific Vocabulary** ⒶⒸⓉ

Reread the fourth paragraph. Write the word that means almost the same as *gazed*.

_____

What happens when Peter gazes at the dream catcher?

2 **Comprehension**

Sequence

Reread the fourth paragraph. What does Peter do after he and Nokomis make a dream catcher? Underline the sentence that tells what he does.

COLLABORATE

3 **Talk About It**

How do you think Peter feels about his presentation the next morning?

Justify your answer. _____

Peter felt disappointment because he wanted to **share** the dream catcher with his class.

"We could make you one," said Nokomis.

"I'd like that!" cried Peter.

Nokomis and Peter worked together and made a dream catcher. That night, as he **gazed** and looked at the dream catcher over his bed, he made a plan.

The next morning he told Nokomis his plan. "I'm going to show my class how to make a dream catcher," he said.

ELD.PI.3.6.Ex, ELD.PI.3.6.Br, ELD.PII.3.1.Ex, ELD.PII.3.1.Br, ELD.PII.3.2a.Ex, ELD.PII.3.2a.Br, ELD.PII.3.2b.Ex, ELD.PII.3.2b.Br See the California Standards section.

"That's a great idea!" said Nokomis. "Let's celebrate after your presentation. I will bake corn cookies and we will have a **traditional** Ojibwe party."

Peter shared his dream catcher with his classmates and showed them how to make their own. Peter didn't feel **nervous** or scared at all. He felt **pride** in his culture. He felt pride in himself, too.

Make Connections

? What tradition does Peter learn about? How does it help him? **ESSENTIAL QUESTION**

What traditions do you take part in? **TEXT TO SELF**

Richard Johnson

ELD.PI.3.6.Ex, ELD.PI.3.6.Br See the California Standards section.

37

Text Evidence

1 **Specific Vocabulary** **A C T**

Circle the word *traditional* in the first paragraph. Write the root word you see in *traditional*.

_____

Underline something traditional in the paragraph.

2 **Sentence Structure** **A C T**

Look at the first sentence in the second paragraph. Circle the subject. Underline the two actions that the subject does.

COLLABORATE

3 **Talk About It**

Why does Peter feel pride in his culture and pride in himself? Discuss your ideas.

_____

_____

_____

Respond to the Text

COLLABORATE

Partner Discussion Work with a partner. Answer the questions. Discuss what you learned about "The Dream Catcher." Write the page numbers where you found text evidence.

Why does Peter need to find a family tradition?

I learned that Peter feels sad because _____.

I read that Nokomis makes Peter feel better by _____

_____.

In the story, Nokomis and Peter make _____.

Text Evidence 🔍

Page(s): _____

Page(s): _____

Page(s): _____

How does Peter use the dream catcher?

In the story, Peter teaches his class _____

_____.

At the end of the story, Peter feels _____

_____.

Text Evidence 🔍

Page(s): _____

Page(s): _____

COLLABORATE

Group Discussion Present your answers to the group. Cite text evidence to justify your thinking. Listen to and discuss the group's opinions about your answers.

ELD.PI.3.2.Ex, ELD.PI.3.2.Br, ELD.PI.3.3.Ex, ELD.PI.3.3.Br, ELD.PI.3.6.Ex, ELD.PI.3.6.Br See the California Standards section.

Write Work with a partner. Review your notes about "The Dream Catcher." Then write your answer to the Essential Question. Use text evidence to support your answer. Use vocabulary words from this week's reading in your writing.

How does the dream catcher teach Peter about traditions in his culture?

Peter needs to give a presentation about _____

_____ .

Nokomis shows Peter _____ .

Peter teaches his class _____

_____ .

Peter's presentation about a tradition makes him feel _____

_____ .

Share Writing Present your writing to the class. Discuss their opinions. Think about what the class has to say. Did they justify their claims? Explain why you agree or disagree with their claims. You can say:

I agree with _____ .

That's a good comment, but _____ .

Write to Sources

pages 32–37

Walter

Take Notes About the Text I took notes on this chart to respond to the prompt: *Add a descriptive paragraph about the story. Describe what happens in Peter's dream after he makes the dream catcher.*

> Nokomis showed Peter her dream catcher.

⬇

> Nokomis and Peter made a new dream catcher.

⬇

> Peter looked at the dream catcher over his bed that night.

Write About the Text **I used my notes to write a descriptive paragraph. It describes Peter's dream.**

Student Model: *Narrative Text*

Peter went to sleep. He had a dream. He was walking in the woods. He saw a big spider! The spider chased Peter and tried to catch him. Peter was scared. Then Peter noticed his dream catcher under a tree. Peter picked up the dream catcher, and the spider ran away!

TALK ABOUT IT

COLLABORATE

Text Evidence

Draw a box around the sentence that tells how Peter feels. Why does Walter include this detail?

Grammar

Circle a doing verb that shows action. Why does Walter use this doing verb?

Connect Ideas

Underline the word that connects the two parts in the fifth sentence. Who does the pronoun *him* refer to?

Your Turn

COLLABORATE

Add a paragraph to the end of the story. Write about what happens after Peter's school presentation.

>> *Go Digital*
Write your response online. Use your editing checklist.

ELD.PI.3.10a.Ex, ELD.PI.3.10a.Br, ELD.PII.3.2a.Ex, ELD.PII.3.2a.Br, ELD.PII.3.3.Ex, ELD.PII.3.3.Br, ELD.PII.3.6.Ex, ELD.PII.3.6.Br See the California Standards section.

TALK ABOUT IT

Weekly Concept Communities

? **Essential Question**
How do people from different
cultures contribute to a community?

>> *Go Digital*

42

COLLABORATE How are the children sharing their cultures? What are people learning? Write the words in the web.

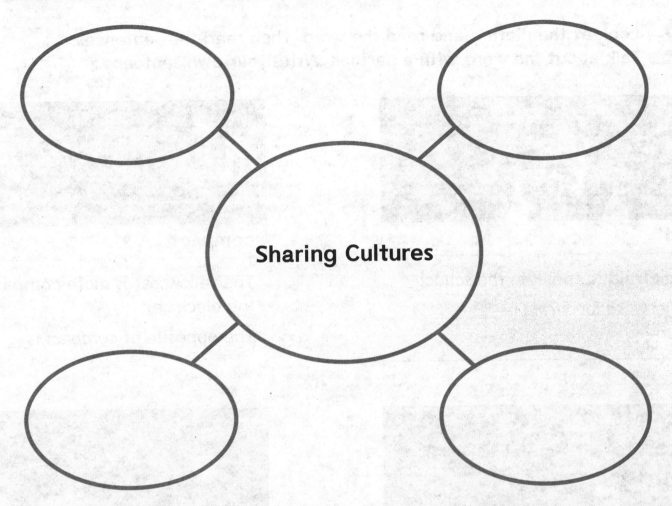

Sharing Cultures

Discuss how the children are sharing their culture with the community. Use the words from the web. You can say:

The children are sharing _____

with the community by _____.

The people are learning _____

ELD.PI.3.1.Ex, ELD.PI.3.1.Br, ELD.PI.3.5.Ex, ELD.PI.3.5.Br, ELD.PI.3.12.Ex, ELD.PI.3.12.Br See the California Standards section.

More Vocabulary

Look at the picture and read the word. Then read the sentences. Talk about the word with a partner. Write your own sentence.

afraid

Sam is **afraid** to speak to the school.

Another word for *afraid* is _____

_____.

agreed

We **agreed** to play a game.

I *agree* with my friends when _____

_____.

compact

The yellow car is more **compact** than the black car.

The opposite of *compact* is _____.

different

Many **different** fish live in the ocean.

I have many *different* _____

_____.

project

The students did this **project** together.

My favorite *project* was _____

_____.

proud

Pat is **proud** because she won the prize.

I feel *proud* when I _____

_____.

Words and Phrases
Indefinite Pronouns

no one = not one person
No one has a big dog.

everyone = all people
Everyone has a cat.

Read the sentences below. Write the indefinite pronoun that means the same as the underlined words.

<u>Not one person</u> was in the park.

_____ was in the park.

Our teacher gave <u>all people</u> a book.

Our teacher gave _____ a book.

>> *Go Digital* **Add these words to your New Words notebook. Write a sentence to show the meaning of each.**

(t)Randy Faris/SuperStock; (b)JupiterImages/Brand X/Alamy

COLLABORATE

1 Talk About It

Look at the picture. Read the title. Talk about what you see. Write your ideas.

Why do you think the story's title is "Room to Grow"?

_____

_____

_____

Who are the characters? What are they doing?

_____

_____

_____

Take notes as you read the text.

Room to Grow

Essential Question

? How do people from different cultures contribute to a community?

Read how one family helps their community grow.

Our new home in Portland

46

ELD.PI.3.1.Ex, ELD.PI.3.1.Br, ELD.PI.3.3.Ex, ELD.PI.3.3.Br See the California Standards section.

Spring in the City

My name is Kiku Sato. Last spring, my family and I moved from the country to the big city.

Our new home in Portland had no yard. There wasn't even a tiny **plot** of land. So Mama made an indoor garden. First she and Papa planted seeds in pots. Then they hung them from hooks. Next they crammed plants onto shelves. Green vines tumbled over desks. Soon our house had plants everywhere.

At first, I was scared to start school. I was **afraid** no one would be my friend. But I soon met a classmate. Jill Hernandez and I were practicing reading aloud one day. She helped me say her last name, and I helped her pronounce mine. The next day we were best friends. Jill spent lots of time at my house.

A map of Oregon

OREGON

PENDLETON
PORTLAND
★ SALEM
EUGENE
ASHLAND

KEY
• CITY
★ CAPITAL
~ RIVER

(flowers) Japack/amanaimagesRF/Corbis; (bkgd) Wetzel and Company; (c) Margaret Lindmark

ELD.PI.3.1.Ex, ELD.PI.3.1.Br, ELD.PI.3.6.Ex, ELD.PI.3.6.Br, ELD.PI.3.7.Ex, ELD.PI.3.7.Br, ELD.PI.3.8.Ex, ELD.PI.3.8.Br, ELD.PI.3.12.Ex, ELD.PI.3.12.Br, ELD.PII.3.2a.Ex, ELD.PII.3.2a.Br, ELD.PII.3.2b.Ex, ELD.PII.3.2b.Br See the California Standards section.

Text Evidence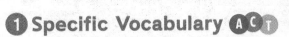

1 **Specific Vocabulary** **A C T**

A *plot* is an area of ground. Reread the second sentence in the second paragraph. What words mean the same as *small area of ground*? Circle the words.

2 **Comprehension**

Sequence

Reread the second paragraph. Circle the signal words that show the order of events. What do Mama and Papa do first to make an indoor garden?

_____

_____

3 **Sentence Structure** **A C T**

Reread the last paragraph. The pronoun *we* refers to more than one person. Who does *we* refer to? Write the words.

_____

47

Circle the quotation marks in the third sentence of the first paragraph. Underline the words that show who is speaking. Circle what the person says.

Reread the second paragraph. The word *serve* means "to bring food or drinks." Underline the sentence that shows what *served* means.

What does Mama do before she adds hot water? Underline the sentence that tells you. What does Mama do after she adds hot water? Circle the sentence that tells you.

An idea for a garden

One afternoon, Jill and her mother came to visit Mama and Papa and me. First they saw our beautiful potted plants. Jill's mother said, "Jill admires your indoor garden. She has told me so much about it."

We all sat down while Mama **served** tea. First she put green tea into the tea bowl. Then she added hot water and stirred. She handed the bowl to Jill's mother and bowed.

Mama's special tea bowls

ELD.PI.3.1.Ex, ELD.PI.3.1.Br, ELD.PI.3.6.Ex, ELD.PI.3.6.Br, ELD.PI.3.12.Ex, ELD.PI.3.12.Br, ELD.PII.3.1.Ex, ELD.PII.3.1.Br, ELD.PII.3.2b.Ex, ELD.PII.3.2b.Br See the California Standards section.

Grandmother in Japan

"My mother **taught** me how to make tea," said Mama. "She also taught me how to plant a traditional Japanese garden. I learned to make the most of a small, **compact** space."

All of a sudden, Jill's mother smiled. "Can you help us with a **project**?" she asked. "Our community wants to plant a garden. Our plot is very small. There is so much we want to grow."

Papa looked at Mama, and they both bowed.

"Yes," they said.

ELD.PI.3.1.Ex, ELD.PI.3.1.Br, ELD.PI.3.6.Ex, ELD.PI.3.6.Br, ELD.PI.3.11.Ex, ELD.PI.3.11.Br, ELD.PI.3.12.Ex, ELD.PI.3.12.Br, ELD.P.II.3.4.Ex, ELD.P.II.3.4.Br See the California Standards section.

Text Evidence

1 Specific Vocabulary A C T

The word *taught* means "showed how." Reread the first paragraph. Underline two things that Grandmother taught Mama to do.

2 Sentence Structure A C T

Adjectives add detail to a sentence. Look at the first paragraph. Underline the adjectives that tell what kind of space Mama had.

COLLABORATE

3 Talk About It

Why does Jill's mother ask Kiku's mother to help? Do you think Kiku's mother can help? Why or why not?

Write your ideas. Justify your answer.

_____

_____

_____

❶ Comprehension

Sequence

Reread the first paragraph. Write the two things Kiku and her family do in sequence. Circle the signal words that tell when things happen.

_____

_____

❷ Specific Vocabulary Ⓐ Ⓒ Ⓣ

The word *shade* means "area with little light." Reread the second paragraph. Circle the word that means the opposite of *shade*.

COLLABORATE

❸ Talk About It

Discuss what Mama and Papa do to make the garden. Is this a good plan? Why or why not?

_____

A Garden Grows

First we had a meeting with the community. Everyone **agreed** to contribute. Some people brought seeds, tools, and dirt. Then the next day we met and started our garden.

Papa built long, open boxes. Next, we filled them with dirt. The tallest box went close to the back wall. The boxes got shorter and shorter. The shortest box was in the front. "All the plants will get sunlight without making **shade** for the others," Mama said.

Papa builds boxes

Jill and I plant seeds

ELD.PI.3.1.Ex, ELD.PI.3.1.Br, ELD.PI.3.6.Ex, ELD.PI.3.6.Br, ELD.PI.3.11.Ex, ELD.PI.3.11.Br, ELD.PI.3.12.Ex, ELD.PI.3.12.Br, ELD.PII.3.1.Ex, ELD.PII.3.1.Br, ELD.PII.3.2b.Ex, ELD.PII.3.2b.Br See the California Standards section.

Then, we used round, flat stones to make a rock path. Papa said that in Japan, stones are an important part of a garden. Finally, we planted the seeds.

Jill and I worked in the garden all summer. Our community grew many **different** vegetables. At the end of the summer, we picked enough vegetables to have a cookout. Mama brought a big pot of miso and vegetable stew. Everyone thanked Mama and Papa for their help. They brought a bit of Japan to Portland. I was so **proud**.

Look what we picked!

Make Connections

? How did Kiku's family help their new community? What parts of their culture did they share? **ESSENTIAL QUESTION**

How can you and your family contribute to your community? **TEXT TO SELF**

1 Comprehension

Sequence

Look at the first paragraph. What happens last? Circle the signal word that tells you. Write what happens last.

_____

2 Sentence Structure Ⓐ Ⓒ Ⓣ

Reread the third sentence in the second paragraph. A comma breaks the sentence into two parts. Circle the comma. Underline what happens at the end of summer.

COLLABORATE

3 Talk About It

How do Kiku and her family bring Japan to Portland?

Justify your answer. _____

_____

_____

(flowers) Japack/amanaimagesRF/Corbis; (bkgd) Wetzel and Company; (c) Margaret Lindmark

ELD.PI.3.1.Ex, ELD.PI.3.1.Br, ELD.PI.3.6.Ex, ELD.PI.3.6.Br, ELD.PI.3.8.Ex, ELD.PI.3.8.Br, ELD.PI.3.12.Ex, ELD.PI.3.12.Br, ELD.PII.3.1.Ex, ELD.PII.3.1.Br, ELD.PII.3.2b.Ex, ELD.PII.3.2b.Br
See the California Standards section.

Respond to the Text

Partner Discussion Work with a partner. Answer the questions. Discuss what you learned about "Room to Grow." Write the page numbers where you found text evidence.

What does Kiku tell us about her family's culture?

I read that Kiku's family makes _____.

Then Kiku's mother serves _____

_____.

According to Kiku, Mama knows how to _____

_____.

Text Evidence 🔍

Page(s): _____

Page(s): _____

Page(s): _____

How does Kiku's family contribute to the community?

Jill's mother asks Kiku's family to _____.

According to Kiku, she and her family make _____.

At the end of the summer, the community _____ and

Mama brings _____.

Text Evidence 🔍

Page(s): _____

Page(s): _____

Page(s): _____

Group Discussion Present your answers to the group. Cite text evidence to justify your thinking. Listen to and discuss the group's opinions about your answers.

 ELD.PI.3.1.Ex, ELD.PI.3.1.Br, ELD.PI.3.2.Ex, ELD.PI.3.2.Br, ELD.PI.3.3.Ex, ELD.PI.3.3.Br, ELD.PI.3.6.Ex, ELD.PI.3.6.Br See the California Standards section.

COLLABORATE

Write Work with a partner. Review your notes about "Room to Grow." Then write your answer to the Essential Question. Use text evidence to support your answer. Use vocabulary words from this week's reading in your writing.

How do Kiku and her family contribute to their community?

Kiku's family knows _____.

Jill's mother asks Kiku's family _____

_____.

Kiku's family builds _____.

The community grows _____.

Jill and Kiku _____.

At the end of the summer, _____.

Mama brings _____.

COLLABORATE

Share Writing Present your writing to the class. Discuss their opinions. Think about what the class has to say. Did they justify their claims? Explain why you agree or disagree with their claims.

I agree with _____.

That's a good comment, but _____.

Write to Sources

pages 46–51

Take Notes About the Text I took notes about the text on this chart. I will answer the question: *What point does the author make in this story?*

Gina

> People bring seeds, tools, and dirt to the community garden.

> Mama and Papa show the community how to plant a small garden.

> At the end of the summer, the community picks vegetables for a cookout.

Write About the Text I used my notes. I wrote an informative paragraph to explain the author's point.

Student Model: *Informative Text*

    The author makes a point in her story. People can do a lot when they work together. Mama and Papa help the community. First, they show people how to grow plants in a small garden. Then everyone works together. Finally, the people pick many vegetables. They have a cookout!

TALK ABOUT IT

Text Evidence

Circle a sentence that comes from the notes. Which word in the sentence tells when it happens?

Grammar

Draw a box around a noun that ends in *-s*. What does the *-s* tell you about the noun?

Connect Ideas

Underline the sentences that tell what happens at the end. How can you combine the sentences to connect the ideas?

Your Turn

How does Kiku's community work together? Use text evidence in your writing.

>> *Go Digital*
Write your response online. Use your editing checklist.

ELD.PI.3.10a.Ex, ELD.PI.3.10a.Br, ELD.PI.3.10b.Ex, ELD.PI.3.10b.Br, ELD.PII.3.2b.Ex, ELD.PII.3.2b.Br, ELD.PII.3.4.Ex, ELD.PII.3.4.Br, ELD.PII.3.6.Ex, ELD.PII.3.6.Br

See the California Standards section. **55**

Weekly Concept Inventions

? **Essential Question**
How can problem solving lead
to new ideas?

>> *Go Digital*

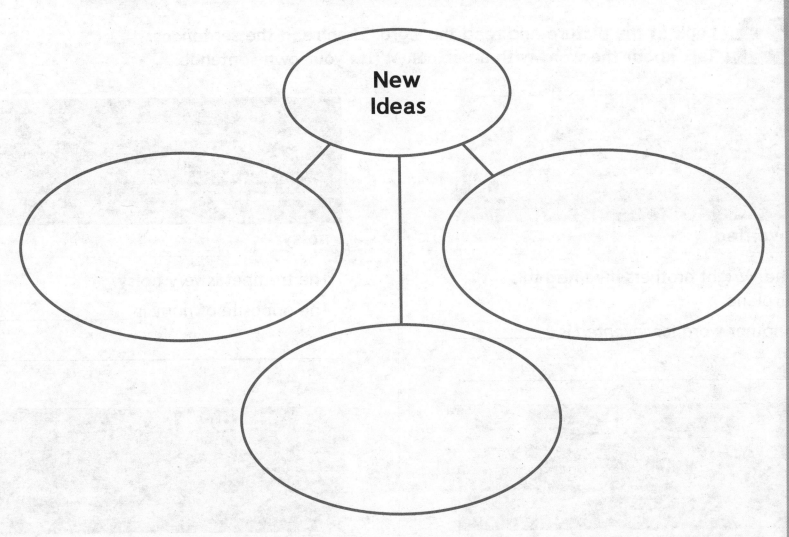

COLLABORATE What is the boy looking at? What is the robot doing? Why is this a new idea? Write the words in the web.

New Ideas

Discuss the new idea in the picture. What problem does the robot solve? Use the words from the web. You can say:

The robot _____. It is a good idea

because _____.

ELD.PI.3.1.Ex, ELD.PI.3.1.Br, ELD.PI.3.5.Ex, ELD.PI.3.5.Br, ELD.PI.3.12.Ex, ELD.PI.3.12.Br See the California Standards section.

More Vocabulary

Look at the picture and read the word. Then read the sentences. Talk about the word with a partner. Write your own sentence.

invented

The Wright brothers **invented** this airplane.

Another word for *invented* is _____

_____.

model

Tom and Dad make a **model** of a car.

I want to make a *model* of _____

_____.

noisy

The trumpet is very **noisy**.

The opposite of *noisy* is _____

_____

repel

My boots **repel** water.

I wear a coat that *repels* water because

_____.

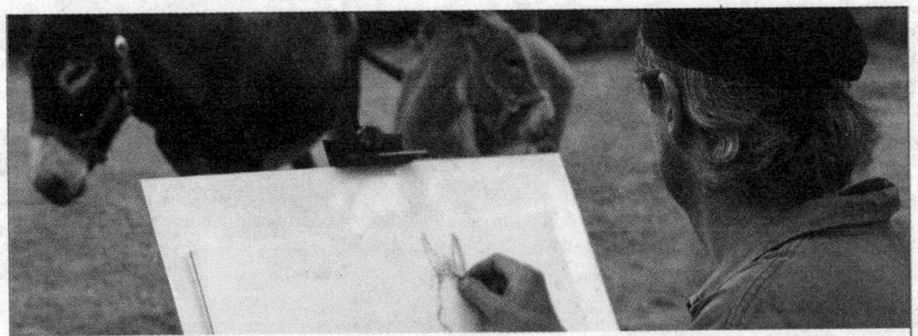

sketched

The artist **sketched** two donkeys.

Artists also *sketch* ___________ because

___________________________________.

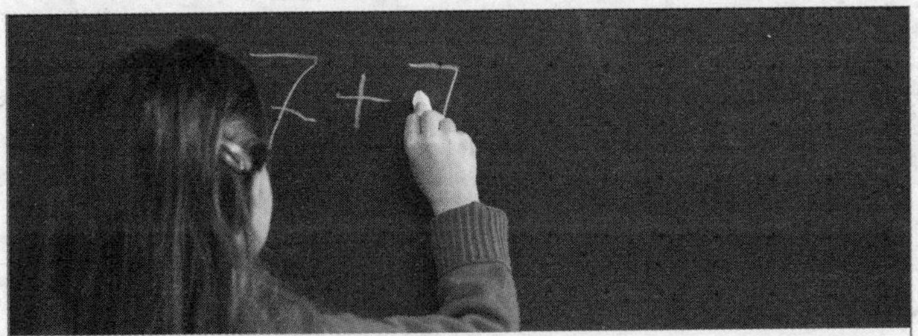

solved

Jane **solved** the problem quickly.

I *solved* a problem by ______________

___________________________________.

Words and Phrases
work and *work out*

work **= does what it needs to do**
Dad fixed my watch, so it works now.

work out **= make**
We will work out a plan to go to the beach.

Read the sentences below. Write the word that means the same as the underlined word or words.

I am happy when my computer does what it needs to do.

I am happy when my computer ______________.

We will make a plan for a class trip.

We will ______________ a plan for a class trip.

» Go Digital **Add these words to your New Words notebook. Write a sentence to show the meaning of each.**

(t)Alexander Klemm/E+/Getty Images; (b)Westend61/SuperStock

COLLABORATE

1 Talk About It

Read the title. Discuss what you see. Write your ideas.

What is a biography? Who is this biography about?

_____

_____

_____

_____

What do you think the title means?

_____

_____

_____

Take notes as you read the text.

Mary Anderson's
GREAT
INVENTION

Essential Question

? **How can problem solving lead to new ideas?**

Read about how someone solved a problem and invented something new.

ELD.PI.3.1.Ex, ELD.PI.3.1.Br, ELD.PI.3.6.Ex, ELD.PI.3.6.Br See the California Standards section.

You might think that a ride in a bus or car is the same today as it was long ago. That isn't true. The first cars were not as fast. They were **noisy**. Cars didn't even have windshield wipers!

When it rained, drivers **rubbed** their windshields with an onion. The oil from the onion would **repel**, or keep off, rain and sleet. It wasn't the best solution, but there were no better substitutes. Nothing else worked. Then a woman named Mary Anderson **solved** the problem.

Malene Laugesen

ELD.PI.3.1.Ex, ELD.PI.3.1.Br, ELD.PI.3.6.Ex, ELD.PI.3.6.Br, ELD.PI.3.7.Ex, ELD.PI.3.7.Br, ELD.PII.3.2b.Ex, ELD.PII.3.2b.Br **See the California Standards section.**

Text Evidence

1 Sentence Structure Ⓐ Ⓒ Ⓣ

Reread the first sentence. What might you think is the same today and long ago? Underline the words that tell what the author is comparing.

2 Specific Vocabulary Ⓐ Ⓒ Ⓣ

The word *rub* means "to move something back and forth." Reread the first sentence of the second paragraph. Why did the drivers rub their windshields with onions?

_____

_____

COLLABORATE

3 Talk About It

Discuss how cars from long ago are different from cars today. Underline three ways that cars from long ago are different.

Text Evidence

1 Sentence Structure A C T

Reread the second sentence in the first paragraph. Circle the comma. Underline what Mary did in the winter of 1902.

2 Comprehension

Cause and Effect

Read the last sentence in the first paragraph. Draw a box around the signal word that shows a cause. Underline two reasons that tell why Mary rode a streetcar.

COLLABORATE

3 Talk About It

Describe what the streetcar driver did to see better. Why were his nose and ears ice cubes?

_____

_____

_____

It Started with Snow

Mary Anderson grew up in Alabama. In the winter of 1902, she went to New York City. It was a cold and windy day. The sky was a gray curtain. Snow was a white blanket on the ground. Mary was cold and wet. Because she wanted to warm up and get dry, she rode a streetcar.

Back then, some streetcar windshields had two parts. They opened with a push. From her seat, Mary watched snow and ice build up on the windshield. The streetcar driver could not see. So, he pushed open the windshield. This helped him to see better. As a result, snow and ice blew in his face. Soon his nose and ears were ice cubes.

Other cars kept stopping, too. Sometimes the drivers hopped out. They wiped off their windshields. Then, they got back in and drove. As a result, traffic moved slowly.

ELD.PI.3.1.Ex, ELD.PI.3.1.Br, ELD.PI.3.6.Ex, ELD.PI.3.6.Br, ELD.PII.3.6.Ex, ELD.PII.3.6.Br
See the California Standards section.

The Next Step

Mary thought about this problem. How could drivers clean their windshields without stopping? Could they do it without opening their windshield?

Back home in Alabama, Mary **sketched** her idea. Then she added notes. She wanted to examine her solution to make sure that it worked. Next, Mary did her own **investigation**. She looked for facts about what drivers needed. She **invented** a windshield wiper that a driver could use from inside the car. Then she worked out a design, or plan. On paper, Mary's invention looked simple. She hoped drivers would find it easy to use.

Mary Anderson's Windshield Wiper

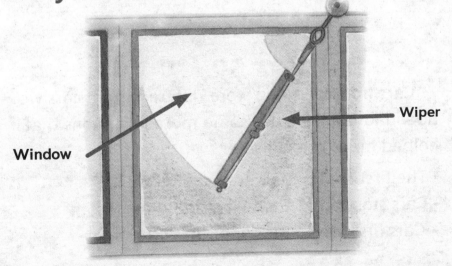

Window

Wiper

The first windshield wiper was moved by a handle inside the car.

1 Specific Vocabulary A C T

Read the second paragraph. An *investigation* is when someone searches to get information. Underline the sentence that tells what Mary did in her investigation.

2 Sentence Structure A C T

Look at sentence six in the second paragraph. Underline the words that tell what Mary invented. Box the words that tell you who used her invention. Circle the words that tell you where the drivers used the invention.

COLLABORATE

3 Talk About It

Discuss why a windshield wiper is a helpful invention for drivers.

_____

_____

Malene Laugesen

ELD.PI.3.1.Ex, ELD.PI.3.1.Br, ELD.PI.3.6.Ex, ELD.PI.3.6.Br, ELD.PI.3.12.Ex, ELD.PI.3.12.Br, ELD.PII.3.2a.Ex, ELD.PII.3.2a.Br See the California Standards section.

1 Sentence Structure Ⓐ Ⓒ Ⓣ

Read the second sentence in the first paragraph. Circle the commas. These commas separate things in a list. What was the model made from? Underline the words.

2 Comprehension

Cause and Effect

Read the fifth and sixth sentences in the first paragraph. What happened when the driver moved the handle? Circle the words that tell you.

3 Talk About It

Why didn't people use Mary's windshield wipers? Why did windshield wipers begin to sell in 1913?

_____

_____

Mary had a **model** built. It was made of quality wood, rubber, and metal. Soon the model was ready to test. It was fitted on a windshield. The driver moved a handle inside the car. The handle caused a blade to move back and forth across the glass. It worked! Mary's idea was a gem! She felt encouraged and was sure it would sell.

Solving the Problem

Mary's windshield wipers solved a problem. But it took many years before people used them. That's because most people did not own cars.

By 1913, more people bought and drove cars. Those cars had windshields. Finally windshield wipers began to sell. Driving became safer and easier because of Mary Anderson's idea.

Safer to Drive

Cars from long ago were different from cars we ride in today. Here are some more inventions that helped make driving safer.

- The first seat belts were used in 1885.
- Cars stopped at the first stop sign in 1915.
- Cars first used turn signals in 1938.

ELD.PI.3.1.Ex, ELD.PI.3.1.Br, ELD.PI.3.6.Ex, ELD.PI.3.6.Br See the California Standards section.

Make Connections

? Talk about how Mary Anderson's solution to a problem led to a new idea. ESSENTIAL QUESTION

What inventions have made your life better? TEXT TO SELF

ELD.PI.3.1.Ex, ELD.PI.3.1.Br, ELD.PI.3.6.Ex, ELD.PI.3.6.Br, ELD.PII.3.1.Ex, ELD.PII.3.1.Br, ELD.PII.3.6.Ex, ELD.PII.3.6.Br See the California Standards section.

Text Evidence

1 Sentence Structure A C T

A bullet • shows part of a list. Find the bullets on page 64. Circle them. What kind of information do the bullets give? Write your answer.

_____

_____

2 Comprehension

Cause and Effect

Read the information in the box titled "Safer to Drive." List one invention that caused driving to be safer.

_____

COLLABORATE

3 Talk About It

Discuss the inventions that helped make driving safer.

_____

_____

Respond to the Text

Partner Discussion Work with a partner. Answer the questions. Discuss what you learned about "Mary Anderson's Great Invention." Write the page numbers where you found text evidence.

What problem did Mary Anderson see?

Text Evidence 🔍

I read that long ago, cars _____.   Page(s): _____

Based on the text, drivers had to _____.   Page(s): _____

According to the author, traffic moved slowly because _____.   Page(s): _____

How did Mary Anderson's invention solve this problem?

Text Evidence 🔍

Based on the text, Mary invented _____.   Page(s): _____

Mary's invention _____.   Page(s): _____

Drivers were able to _____.   Page(s): _____

People finally used Mary's invention _____.   Page(s): _____

Group Discussion Present your answers to the group. Cite text evidence to justify your thinking. Listen to and discuss the group's opinions about your answers.

ELD.PI.3.1.Ex, ELD.PI.3.1.Br, ELD.PI.3.3.Ex, ELD.PI.3.3.Br, ELD.PI.3.6.Ex, ELD.PI.3.6.Br, ELD.PI.3.11.Ex, ELD.PI.3.11.Br, ELD.PII.3.6.Ex, ELD.PII.3.6.Br See the California Standards section.

Write Work with a partner. Review your notes about "Mary Anderson's Great Invention." Then write your answer to the Essential Question. Use text evidence to support your answer. Use vocabulary words from this week's reading in your writing.

How did Mary Anderson solve a problem and invent something new?

Mary Anderson saw _____. Drivers had to _____.

Mary solved the problem by _____.

Mary's invention helped drivers _____

_____.

Share Writing Present your writing to the class. Discuss their opinions. Think about what the class has to say. Did they justify their claims? Explain why you agree or disagree with their claims.

I agree with _____ because _____.

That's a good comment, but _____.

Write to Sources

bobbieo/E+/Getty Images

David

Take Notes About the Text I took notes on this chart to answer the questions: *What problem did drivers have? How did Mary solve the problem? Explain using text evidence.*

pages 60–65

> Problem: Rain and snow hit windshields. It was hard for drivers to see.

↓

> First, Mary sketched her idea for a windshield wiper.

↓

> Next, Mary made a model of her invention.

↓

> Finally, a driver tested the windshield wiper.

ELD.PI.3.1.Ex, ELD.PI.3.1.Br, ELD.PI.3.6.Ex, ELD.PI.3.6.Br See the California Standards section.

Write About the Text I wrote an informative paragraph about how Mary solved a problem.

Student Model: *Informative Text*

Rain and snow hit windshields. It was hard for drivers to see. Mary decided to solve the problem. First, she sketched her idea for a windshield wiper. Next, she made a model of her invention. Finally, a driver tested the windshield wiper. It worked!

TALK ABOUT IT

COLLABORATE

Text Evidence

Draw a box around the sixth sentence. This sentence comes from the notes. Why does David use the word *finally*?

Grammar

Circle the sentence about rain and snow. What is the predicate of this sentence?

Connect Ideas

Underline the sentences that explain the problem. How can you combine the sentences to connect the ideas?

Your Turn

COLLABORATE

How do people get ideas for inventions? Use evidence from the text to support your answer.

>> Go Digital
Write your response online. Use your editing checklist.

? **Essential Question**

How do landmarks help us
understand our country's story?

≫ *Go Digital*

COLLABORATE

What does this landmark show? What do you learn from landmarks? Write the words in the web.

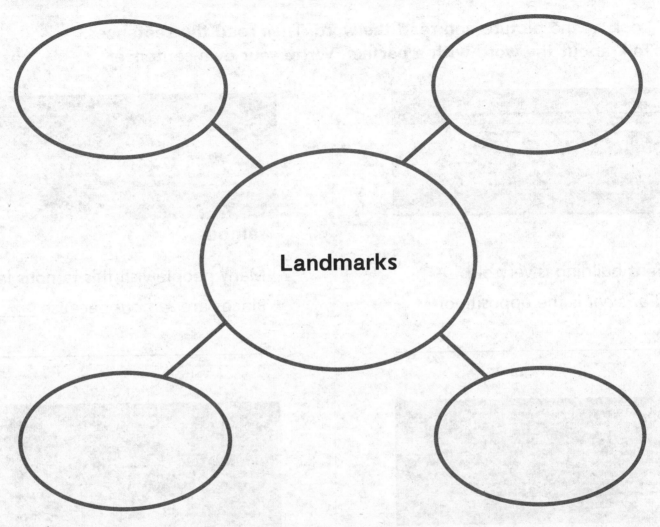

Landmarks

Discuss this landmark. What does it help us understand? Use the words from the web. You can say:

This landmark shows _____. It helps us understand

_____ because _____.

ELD.PI.3.1.Ex, ELD.PI.3.1.Br, ELD.PI.3.5.Ex, ELD.PI.3.5.Br, ELD.PI.3.12.Ex, ELD.PI.3.12.Br See the California Standards section.

More Vocabulary

Look at the picture and read the word. Then read the sentences. Talk about the word with a partner. Write your own sentence.

ancient

This **ancient** building is very old.

The word *ancient* is the opposite of

_____ .

explorers

The **explorers** travel to a new place.

Explorers travel to new places to find

_____ .

famous

Many people visit this **famous** landmark.

Places are *famous* because _____

_____ .

formed

We **formed** the castle from wet sand.

Another word for *formed* is _____

_____ .

ELD.PI.3.1.Ex, ELD.PI.3.1.Br, ELD.PI.3.5.Ex, ELD.PI.3.5.Br, ELD.PI.3.12.Ex, ELD.PI.3.12.Br See the California Standards section.

protect

The helmets **protect** our heads.

Another word for *protect* is _____

_____.

treasure

These pictures are a family **treasure**.

My favorite *treasure* is my _____

_____.

Words and Phrases
Homophones

there = tells where something is
I put my backpack <u>there</u> on the chair.

their = belongs to them
Max and Ana are working on <u>their</u> project.

Read the sentences below. Underline the homophone *there* or their in each sentence.

They put their cups in the sink.

The pens are there on the desk.

The girls read their books.

Write your own sentences using *there* and *their*.

>> Go Digital Add *their* and *there* to your New Words notebook. Write a sentence to show the meaning of each.

1 Talk About It

Read the title. Discuss what you see. Write your ideas.

Why do you think the author chose this title?

_____

_____

_____

_____

How are the picture and the title connected?

_____

_____

_____

_____

Take notes as you read the text.

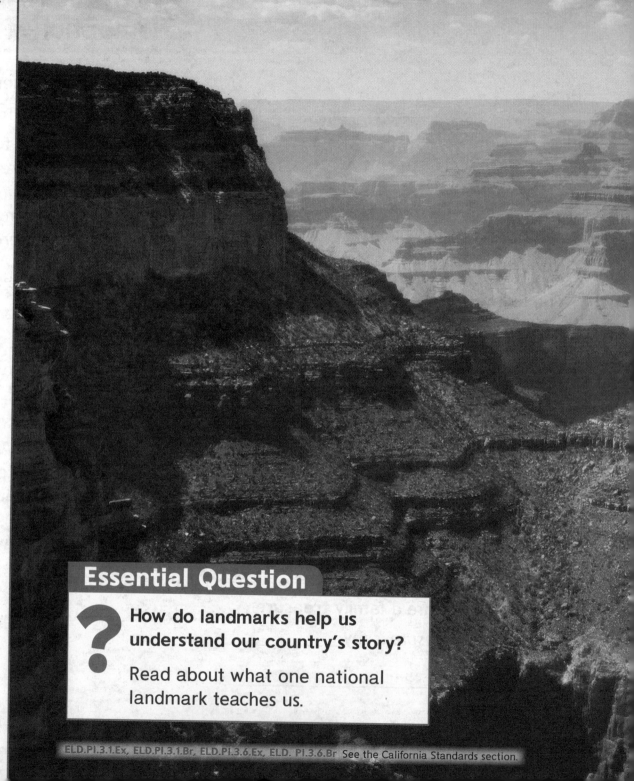

Essential Question

? **How do landmarks help us understand our country's story?**

Read about what one national landmark teaches us.

ELD.PI.3.1.Ex, ELD.PI.3.1.Br, ELD.PI.3.6.Ex, ELD. PI.3.6.Br See the California Standards section.

A Natural Beauty

It is a **famous** landmark in the United States, and it's **huge**! It is one mile deep and ten miles wide. It was carved out of rock by the Colorado River. It stretches across parts of four states. What is it? It's the Grand Canyon!

Exploring the Canyon

Many tourists visit the Grand Canyon. In fact, almost five million people take a trip to this national **treasure** each year. People come from around the world to hike the dusty trails. They take boat rides down the Colorado River. They gaze across miles of massive red and brown cliffs.

Nature lovers visit the Grand Canyon, too. They come to look for animals. They peek at the hundreds of different kinds of plants. They may spot eagles and see mountain lions. They may spy snakes and spiders, and some may even see bats. Some visitors also come to learn about the canyon's history.

ELD.PI.3.1.Ex, ELD.PI.3.1.Br, ELD.PI.3.6.Ex, ELD.PI.3.6.Br, ELD.PI.3.7.Ex, ELD.PI.3.7.Br, ELD.PI.3.8.Ex, ELD.PI.3.8.Br, ELD.PII.3.1.Ex, ELD.PII.3.1.Br, ELD.PII.3.7.Ex, ELD.PII.3.7.Br See the California Standards section.

Text Evidence

1 Specific Vocabulary Ⓐ Ⓒ Ⓣ

The word *huge* means "very big." Circle the word *huge*. Underline clues in the text that tell why the Grand Canyon is huge.

2 Comprehension

Main Idea and Details

Reread the second paragraph. Why do tourists visit the Grand Canyon? Underline three details that support this main idea.

3 Sentence Structure Ⓐ Ⓒ Ⓣ

Look at the fourth sentence in the last paragraph. Circle the connecting word *and*. Write the two actions that the word *and* connects.

_____

_____

1 Sentence Structure ACT

Reread the first sentence of the first paragraph. Underline the date that tells when explorers first saw the Grand Canyon.

2 Specific Vocabulary ACT

The word *discover* means "to see or find something for the first time." What did American explorers discover in 1857?

_____

COLLABORATE

3 Talk About It

Discuss two things scientists found in the Grand Canyon. Why were these important discoveries?

_____

_____

History of the Canyon

Explorers from Europe first saw the Grand Canyon in 1540. Then in 1857, American explorers **discovered** it. They found groups of Native Americans living there. One of these groups was the **Ancient** Pueblo people.

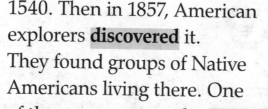

The Ancient Pueblo people lived in cliff houses like these.

The Ancient Pueblo people lived in the canyon for almost one thousand years. They were farmers and hunters. Scientists have found traces, or parts, of their old homes still standing.

Scientists have also found very old rocks in the Grand Canyon. These rocks are some of the oldest in the world. They are clues to how the canyon was **formed**. Some scientists look for clues about the people who lived there. They have found tools and pieces of pottery.

A Great Big Park — This map shows where the Grand Canyon is.

UTAH

NEVADA

GRAND CANYON NATIONAL PARK

Colorado River

Lake Mead

○ Las Vegas

Colorado River

North Rim

15

Grand Canyon ○ Village

○ City
— Highway
▨ Grand Canyon National Park

ARIZONA

Kingman

40

Flagstaff

(tl) © Canyon Florey/Aurora Photos/Corbis; (bl) Mapping Specialists, Ltd. (r) Matt Dil/Flickr/Getty Images

ELD.PI.3.1.Ex, ELD.PI.3.1.Br, ELD.PI.3.6.Ex, ELD.PI.3.6.Br, ELD.PI.3.8.Ex, ELD.PI.3.8.Br, ELD.PII.3.1.Ex, ELD.PII.3.1.Br See the California Standards section.

It's a Landmark

President Theodore Roosevelt visited the Grand Canyon in 1903. He saw how beautiful it was. He said it was a special place. As a result, he made it a national monument. Then in 1919, the Grand Canyon was **declared** a national park. That means the land is **protected**. No one can build homes on it. The Grand Canyon is a place all Americans can enjoy.

Protect the Canyon

It is important for people to take care of national landmarks. We can do our part by following the rules when we visit. Animals and wildlife are safe there and should not be touched. Rivers must be kept clean.

There is still a lot to learn about this beautiful landmark. It is important that we protect it.

Bighorn sheep live in the Grand Canyon.

Make Connections

How does the Grand Canyon teach us about America's story? ESSENTIAL QUESTION

What do you find most interesting about the Grand Canyon's history? Why? TEXT TO SELF

ELD.PI.3.1.Ex, ELD.PI.3.1.Br, ELD.PI.3.6.Ex, ELD.PI.3.6.Br, ELD.PI.3.7.Ex, ELD.PI.3.7.Br, ELD.PI.3.8.Ex, ELD.PI.3.8.Br, ELD.PII.3.1.Ex, ELD.PII.3.1.Br, ELD.PII.3.6.Ex, ELD.PII.3.6.Br, ELD.PII.3.7.Ex, ELD.PII.3.7.Br See the California Standards section.

Text Evidence

1 Specific Vocabulary Ⓐ Ⓒ Ⓣ

Look at the first paragraph. The word *declare* means "to tell people that something is true." What was declared in 1919?

_____

_____

2 Sentence Structure Ⓐ Ⓒ Ⓣ

Look at the third sentence in "Protect the Canyon." Circle the word that connects the opinions about animals and wildlife. Underline the two opinions.

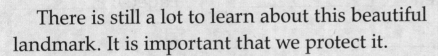

COLLABORATE

3 Talk About It

What is the author's opinion about protecting the Grand Canyon?

_____

_____

Respond to the Text

Partner Discussion Work with a partner. Answer the questions. Discuss what you learned about "A Natural Beauty." Write the page numbers where you found text evidence.

Why is the Grand Canyon a famous landmark?

Many tourists visit _____ because _____.

Based on the text, explorers _____.

According to the author, scientists _____.

Text Evidence 🔍

Page(s): _____

Page(s): _____

Page(s): _____

Why should we protect the Grand Canyon?

According to author, President Roosevelt _____

_____.

The Grand Canyon became a landmark _____.

Based on the text, we protect _____

_____.

Text Evidence 🔍

Page(s): _____

Page(s): _____

Page(s): _____

Group Discussion Present your answers to the group. Cite text evidence to justify your thinking. Listen to and discuss the group's opinions about your answers.

 ELD.PI.3.1.Ex, ELD.PI.3.1.Br, ELD.PI.3.3.Ex, ELD.PI.3.3.Br, ELD.PI.3.6.Ex, ELD.PI.3.6.Br, ELD.PI.3.11.Ex, ELD.PI.3.11.Br, ELD.PII.3.6.Ex, ELD.PII.3.6.Br See the California Standards section.

Write Work with a partner. Review your notes about "A Natural Beauty." Then write your answer to the Essential Question. Use text evidence to support your answer. Use vocabulary words from this week's reading in your writing.

How does the Grand Canyon help us understand our country's story?

Explorers discovered _____

_____.

Scientists found _____

_____.

President Roosevelt visited _____.

As a result, the canyon was declared _____.

Share Writing Present your writing to the class. Discuss their opinions. Think about what the class has to say. Did they justify their claims? Explain why you agree or disagree with their claims.

I agree with _____.

That's a good comment, but _____.

Write to Sources

pages 74–77

Patrick

Take Notes About the Text I took notes about the text to answer the question: *In your opinion, does the author do a good job of showing that the Grand Canyon is an important landmark? Use text evidence in your answer.*

The author says the canyon is a mile deep and ten miles wide.

The author shows that the Grand Canyon is an important landmark.

The author says animals live in the canyon.

The author says people can enjoy nature or learn about history there.

©Hero/Corbis/Glow Images

Write About the Text I used notes from my idea web to write an opinion about the text.

Student Model: *Opinion*

The author does a good job of showing readers that the Grand Canyon is an important landmark. The author says the canyon is a mile deep and ten miles wide! Many animals live there. Some people come to enjoy nature. Other people come to learn about history. These details show me that the Grand Canyon is important.

TALK ABOUT IT

Text Evidence

Draw a box around the sentence that tells the size of the canyon. Why does Patrick use an exclamation point?

Grammar

Circle the sentence about animals. How can you add a word to describe the animals?

Connect Ideas

Underline the sentences that tell why people come to the park. How can you use the word *but* to connect the ideas?

Your Turn

In your opinion, why should the Grand Canyon be protected? Use details from the text in your answer.

>> *Go Digital*
Write your response online. Use your editing checklist.

Unit 2

Figure It Out

The Big Idea

What does it take to solve a problem?

TALK ABOUT IT

Weekly Concept Cooperation

? Essential Question

Why is working together a good way to solve a problem?

>> *Go Digital*

84

What are the friends in the picture doing? Why is it a good way to solve a problem? Write the words in the web.

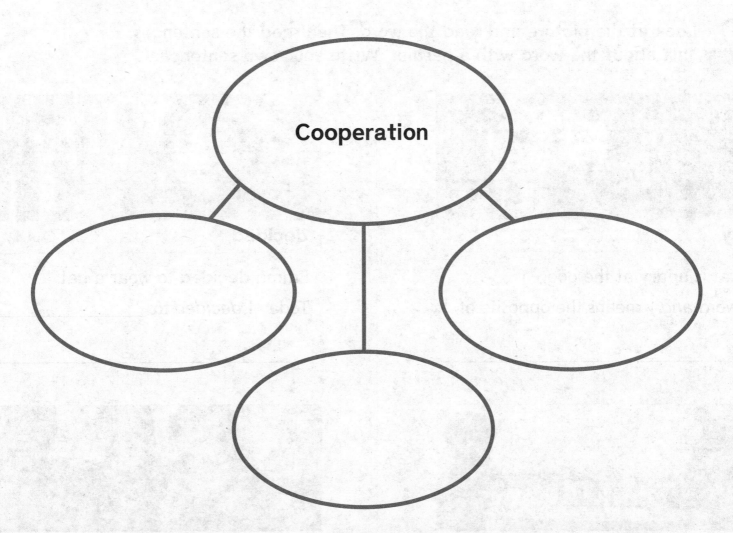

Cooperation

Discuss how these friends are cooperating. How does it help solve a problem? Use the words from the web. You can say:

When friends _____,

it makes the job _____.

Look at the picture and read the word. Then read the sentences. Talk about the word with a partner. Write your own sentence.

COLLABORATE

angry

The cat is **angry** at the dog.

The word *angry* means the opposite of

_____.

decided

Emma **decided** to wear a hat.

Today I *decided* to _____

_____.

clever

Leo is a **clever** player.

I am *clever* when I _____

_____.

filthy

The kids are **filthy**.

The kids are *filthy* because _____

_____.

ELD.PI.3.1.Ex, ELD.PI.3.1.Br, ELD.PI.3.5.Ex, ELD.PI.3.5.Br, ELD.PI.3.12.Ex, ELD.PI.3.12.Br See the California Standards section.

shy

The cat hides because it is **shy**.

I feel shy when I _____

_____ .

wonderful

The bowl of fruit looks **wonderful**.

Another word for *wonderful* is

_____

Words and Phrases
Multiple-meaning words/ Homographs

The word *light* means "not heavy."
I carry a <u>light</u> backpack to school.

The word *light* means "a lamp."
I turned on a <u>light</u> in the dark room.

Read the sentences below. Circle the words that mean the same as the underlined homographs.

The bag is easy to carry because it is <u>light</u>.

not heavy   a lamp

I read with a <u>light</u> at night.

not heavy   a lamp

>> Go Digital Add these homographs to your New Words notebook. Write two sentences to show each meaning of the word *light*.

COLLABORATE

1 Talk About It

Read the title. Discuss what you see. Write your ideas.

What does the title tell you?

_____

_____

_____

_____

Who are characters in the story?

_____

_____

_____

Take notes as you read the story.

Anansi
Learns a Lesson

Essential Question

Why is working together a good way to solve a problem?

Read how Turtle works with a friend to solve his problem.

ELD.PI.3.1.Ex, ELD.PI.3.1.Br, ELD.PI.3.6.Ex, ELD.PI.3.6.Br See the California Standards section.

Anansi the Spider lived alone and made his lunch the same time each day. One afternoon, Turtle stopped by.

"I hate to get in the way and interfere with your meal, but those bananas look **wonderful**," said Turtle. "I am so hungry."

Anansi knew he should share with others. It was a big part of his culture. But he was hungry and didn't want to share. He **decided** to play a trick on Turtle.

1 Sentence Structure Ⓐ Ⓒ Ⓣ

Read the second paragraph. Circle the comma in the first sentence. Underline the word that connects the two clauses. Draw a box around each clause. Why does Turtle interfere with Anansi's meal?

2 Specific Vocabulary Ⓐ Ⓒ Ⓣ

Someone who is sly is able to fool others. Reread the last sentence in the third paragraph. Circle the phrase that is a clue to the meaning of *sly*.

COLLABORATE

3 Talk About It

How does Anansi feel about sharing his food? Justify your answer.

Janet Broxon

ELD.PI.3.1.Ex, ELD.PI.3.1.Br, ELD.PI.3.6.Ex, ELD.PI.3.6.Br, ELD.PI.3.7.Ex, ELD.PI.3.7.Br, ELD.PI.3.8.Ex, ELD.PI.3.8.Br, ELD.PI.3.12.Ex, ELD.PI.3.12.Br See the California Standards section.

Text Evidence

1 Sentence Structure Ⓐ Ⓒ Ⓣ

Look at the first paragraph. Which words show who is asking the question? Underline the words.

2 Specific Vocabulary Ⓐ Ⓒ Ⓣ

Look at the fourth paragraph. *Spoil* means "to become rotten or go bad." Who says the bananas might spoil? Circle the character's name.

3 Comprehension

Theme

You can look at details about characters to find a story's theme. Which character needs to be taught a lesson? Give your opinion. Justify your answer.

_____

_____

_____

"Please, help yourself," Anansi said with a **sly** grin.

Turtle reached for the food. "Shouldn't you wash your hands?" asked Anansi.

"Oh, yes!" Turtle said. When Turtle returned, Anansi had eaten half of the bananas.

"I didn't want the bananas to **spoil**," said Anansi.

Turtle got closer and made another attempt to eat. Anansi stopped him again.

"Turtle, please go wash your hands," he said.

Turtle knew his hands were clean, but Anansi still thought they were **filthy**. However, Turtle was too **shy** and timid to say no. When he returned Anansi had eaten the rest of the fruit.

"Ha, ha, I tricked you, Turtle," said Anansi. "You didn't get any bananas!"

ELD.PI.3.1.Ex, ELD.PI.3.1.Br, ELD.PI.3.6.Ex, ELD.PI.3.6.Br, ELD.PI.3.11.Ex, ELD.PI.3.11.Br
See the California Standards section.

Turtle was **angry** at Anansi. He decided to teach that **nasty** spider a lesson. "Please come to my house at the bottom of the lake for dinner tomorrow," said Turtle.

Anansi quickly said yes. He loved free food.

Turtle couldn't trick Anansi alone, so he decided to ask Fish to get involved and help make a plan.

Turtle found Fish at the lake. "Fish, I need your help," he said. "With your cooperation, we can trick Anansi." Anansi had tricked Fish many times so Fish was happy to help. Together the two friends created a **clever** plan.

Janet Broxon

ELD.PI.3.1.Ex, ELD.PI.3.1.Br, ELD.PI.3.6.Ex, ELD.PI.3.6.Br, ELD.PI.3.7.Ex, ELD.PI.3.7.Br, ELD.PII.3.2a.Ex, ELD.PII.3.2a.Br See the California Standards section.

1 Specific Vocabulary A C T

Look at the first paragraph. The word *nasty* means "not kind and not nice." Why does Turtle think Anansi is a nasty spider?

_____

_____

2 Sentence Structure A C T

Look at the fourth paragraph. The word *so* connects two clauses. Underline the clause that tells what Anansi did to Fish.

COLLABORATE

3 Talk About It

Why do Turtle and Fish create a plan to trick Anansi? Justify your ideas.

_____

_____

1 Sentence Structure ⒶⒸⓉ

Look at the first sentence. Circle the comma that breaks the sentence into two parts. Read each part. Which part tells when Anansi goes to the lake? Underline the words.

2 Specific Vocabulary ⒶⒸⓉ

A *feast* is a large amount of delicious food. What kind of feast does Anansi see?

_____

COLLABORATE

3 Talk About It

What does Fish do to help Turtle? Take notes. Then paraphrase his actions.

_____

_____

_____

The next day, Anansi went to the lake. Fish met him at the water's edge. "Come, Anansi," said Fish. "We will swim to Turtle's house together." Anansi jumped into the water. He was a clumsy and awkward swimmer. He was also very light.

"How will I ever get down to Turtle's house?" he cried.

Fish knew what to say. "Grab some heavy stones. Then you will sink, not float."

Anansi picked up two big stones, jumped into the lake, and sank down, down, down. Fish swam at his side. At Turtle's house, Anansi saw a wonderful **feast** of berries.

ELD.PI.3.1.Ex, ELD.PI.3.1.Br, ELD.PI.3.6.Ex, ELD.PI.3.6.Br, ELD.PI.3.8.Ex, ELD.PI.3.8.Br, ELD.PI.3.10b.Ex, ELD.PI.3.10b.Br See the California Standards section.

"Welcome, Anansi," said Turtle. "Drop those stones and help yourself."

As soon as Anansi dropped the stones, he rocketed to the surface of the lake. Anansi sputtered furiously. "Fish and Turtle tricked me," he cried angrily.

Back at the bottom of the lake, Turtle and Fish laughed and laughed.

"We worked together and taught Anansi a lesson," said Turtle.

"What a good way to solve a problem," said Fish. "Let's eat!"

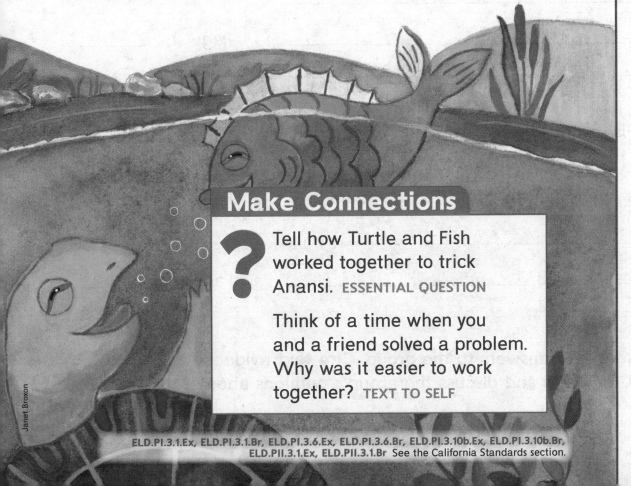

Janet Broxon

Make Connections

? Tell how Turtle and Fish worked together to trick Anansi. ESSENTIAL QUESTION

Think of a time when you and a friend solved a problem. Why was it easier to work together? TEXT TO SELF

ELD.PI.3.1.Ex, ELD.PI.3.1.Br, ELD.PI.3.6.Ex, ELD.PI.3.6.Br, ELD.PI.3.10b.Ex, ELD.PI.3.10b.Br, ELD.PII.3.1.Ex, ELD.PII.3.1.Br See the California Standards section.

Text Evidence

1 Sentence Structure Ⓐ Ⓒ Ⓣ

Reread the first sentence of the second paragraph. Circle the comma. It breaks the sentence into two parts. When does Anansi rocket to the lake's surface? Underline the sentence part that tells you.

COLLABORATE

2 Talk About It

How do you know that Anansi is upset? Use text evidence to support your answer.

_____

_____

_____

3 Comprehension

Theme

Reread the fourth and fifth paragraphs. Which sentences tell the story's theme? Draw a box around the sentences.

Respond to the Text

COLLABORATE

Partner Discussion Work with a partner. Answer the questions. Discuss what you learned about "Anansi Learns a Lesson." Write the page numbers where you found text evidence.

What problem does Turtle have?

I read that Anansi tells Turtle to _____.

Based on the story, Anansi is sly because _____

_____.

Turtle needs to _____.

Text Evidence 🔍

Page(s): _____

Page(s): _____

Page(s): _____

How do Turtle and Fish work together to teach Anansi a lesson?

In the story, Fish tells Anansi he can get to Turtle's house by

_____.

When Anansi releases the rocks, _____.

Text Evidence 🔍

Page(s): _____

Page(s): _____

COLLABORATE

Group Discussion Present your answers to the group. Cite text evidence to justify your thinking. Listen to and discuss the group's opinions about your answers.

COLLABORATE

Write Work with a partner. Review your notes about "Anansi Learns a Lesson." Then write your answer to the Essential Question. Use text evidence to support your answer. Use vocabulary words from this week's reading in your writing.

How do Turtle and Fish work together to teach Anansi a lesson?

Turtle wants to trick Anansi because _____.

Turtle and Fish show cooperation when _____

_____.

Turtle and Fish solve their problem by _____

_____.

COLLABORATE

Share Writing Present your writing to the class. Discuss their opinions. Think about what the class has to say. Did they justify their claims? Explain why you agree or disagree with their claims.

I agree with _____.

That's a good comment, but _____.

Write to Sources

pages 88–93

Luis

Take Notes About the Text I took notes on this chart to respond to the prompt: *Add a paragraph to the end of the story. Have Fish and Turtle tell Anansi why they tricked him.*

Anansi did not want to share his bananas with Turtle.

⬇

Anansi decided to trick Turtle.

⬇

Anansi told Turtle to wash his hands two times.

⬇

Anansi ate all the bananas while Turtle washed his hands.

ELD.PI.3.6.Ex, ELD.PI.3.6.Br See the California Standards section.

Write About the Text I used my chart. I wrote about how Turtle and Fish tell Anansi why they tricked him.

Student Model: *Narrative Text*

"Why did you trick me?" Anansi asked.

Turtle said, "We tricked you because you always trick us."

Anansi said, "When did I trick you?"

Turtle explained. "You did not want to share your bananas. You made me wash my hands two times, and you ate all the bananas."

Fish said, "Now you know how we feel!"

Turtle and Fish laughed. Anansi walked home sadly.

TALK ABOUT IT

COLLABORATE

Text Evidence

Draw a box around the sentence that tells why Turtle and Fish tricked Anansi. Why does Luis use the word *because*?

Grammar

Circle the sentence that tells what Anansi does at the end. Which word tells how Anansi feels when he walks home?

Connect Ideas

Underline the last two sentences. How can you use the word *and* to connect the ideas?

Your Turn

COLLABORATE

Think about Anansi. Add another paragraph to the end of the story. Tell what Anansi does next.

>> Go Digital
Write your response online. Use your editing checklist.

TALK ABOUT IT

Weekly Concept Immigration

? **Essential Question**
Why do people immigrate to new places?

>> Go Digital

COLLABORATE

These immigrants moved to a new place from another country. Why do immigrants move? Write the words in the web.

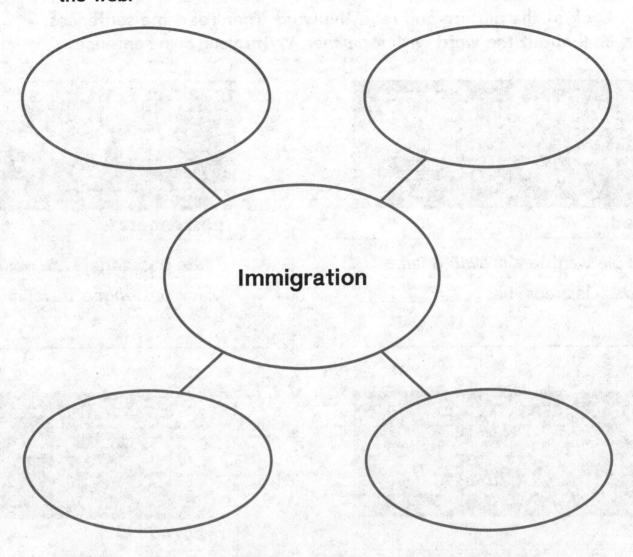

Immigration

Discuss what immigration is. Why do people immigrate to new places? Use the words from the web. You can say:

People immigrate to _____

because _____.

ELD.PI.3.1.Ex, ELD.PI.3.1.Br, ELD.PI.3.5.Ex, ELD.PI.3.5.Br, ELD.PI.3.6.Ex, ELD.PI.3.6.Br See the California Standards section.

99

More Vocabulary

Look at the picture and read the word. Then read the sentences. Talk about the word with a partner. Write your own sentence.

crowded

The people went to a **crowded** fair.

A *crowded* classroom has _____

_____.

passengers

These **passengers** are going on a trip.

Many *passengers* travel in _____

_____.

noticed

Sam **noticed** a bug on the stick.

Today I *noticed* _____

_____.

realized

May **realized** that she was late.

Another word for *realized* is _____

_____.

relax

Lin likes to **relax** under a big tree.

I like to *relax* _____

_____

_____.

voyage

The travelers are going on a **voyage**.

A *voyage* is a very long _____

_____.

Words and Phrases
Idioms with *dream*

land of our dreams = **a perfect place**
America was the <u>land of our dreams</u>.

dream comes true = **when you get something that you really want**
My <u>dream came true</u> when I flew in a jet.

Read the sentences below. Write the phrase that means the same as the underlined words.

I met my favorite baseball player, and <u>it was something I really wanted</u>.

I met my favorite baseball player, and my _____

_____.

We moved to the <u>perfect place</u>.

We moved to the _____

_____.

>> *Go Digital* **Add these idioms with *dream* to your New Words notebook. Write a sentence to show the meaning of each idiom.**

Text Evidence

COLLABORATE

1 Talk About It

Read the title. Discuss what you see. Write your ideas.

What does the title tell you?

____

____

____

____

Who are the characters you see? What are they looking at?

____

____

____

____

Take notes as you read the text.

Shared Read Genre • Historical Fiction

SAILING TO AMERICA

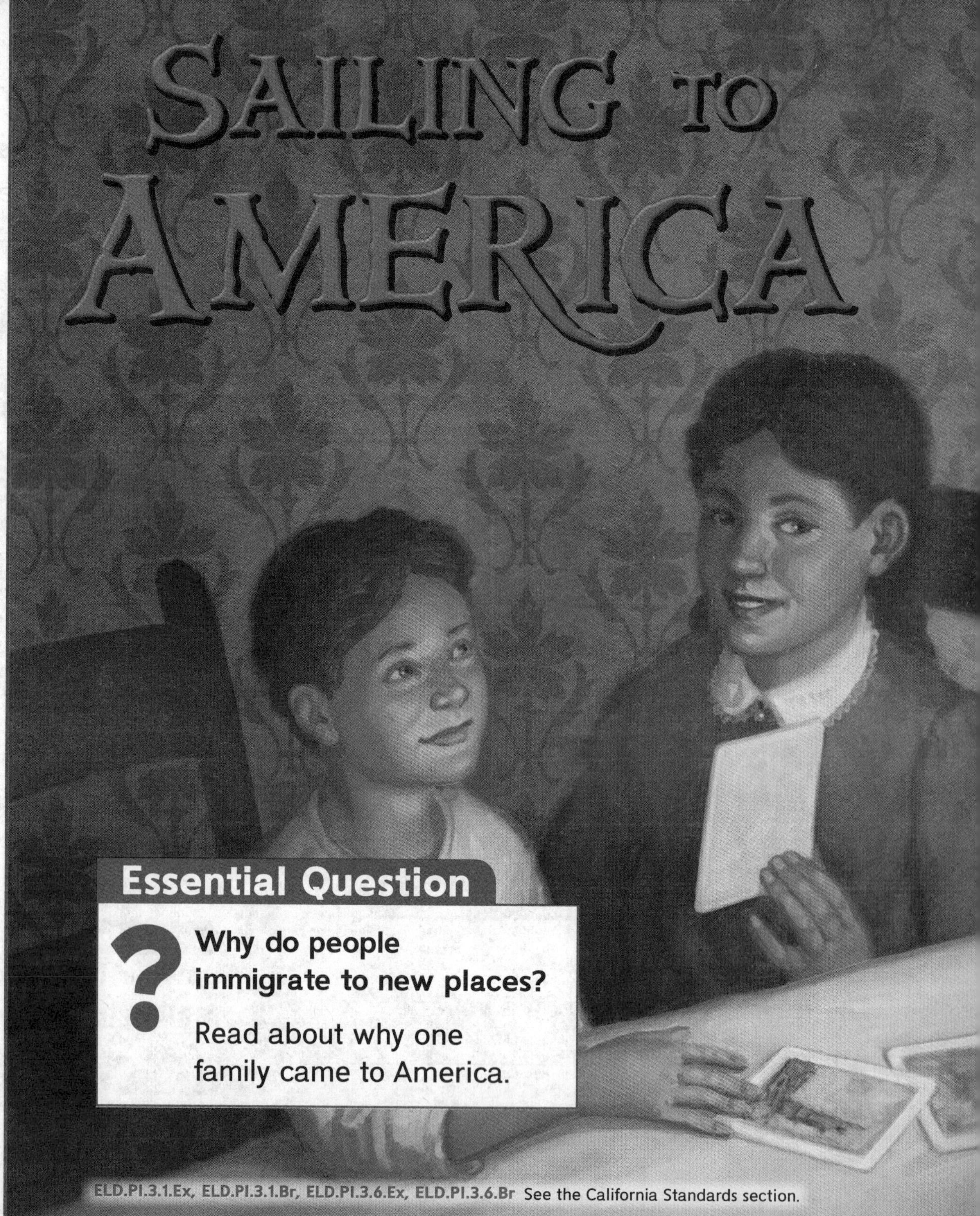

Essential Question

Why do people immigrate to new places?

Read about why one family came to America.

ELD.PI.3.1.Ex, ELD.PI.3.1.Br, ELD.PI.3.6.Ex, ELD.PI.3.6.Br See the California Standards section.

Nora woke early. She hadn't slept much. It was March, 1895. Da was leaving for America today. Uncle Sean immigrated there last year and found work right away. He asked Da to **join** him. It was Mama and Da's dream to one day live in America.

Nora lit a lamp for light and sat down at the table. Her brother, Danny, joined her.

"I feel like crying," he whispered softly.

"I know," Nora answered. "So do I, but this is Da and Mama's dream. Da will find work and send for us. Look at the photographs that Uncle Sean sent. Doesn't America look grand?"

Tristan Elwell

1 Specific Vocabulary A C T

Look at the word *join* in the first paragraph. *Join* means "to go somewhere to be with someone." Who will Da join in America?

_____

2 Sentence Structure A C T

Reread the first sentence of the second paragraph. Circle the word that connects the two actions in the sentence. Underline each action.

COLLABORATE

3 Talk About It

Why is Da going to America?

_____

_____

ELD.PI.3.1.Ex, ELD.PI.3.1.Br, ELD.PI.3.6.Ex, ELD.PI.3.6.Br, ELD.PII.3.6.Ex, ELD.PII.3.6.Br
See the California Standards section.

1 Sentence Structure

Look at the second paragraph. Circle the punctuation marks that show someone is speaking. Who is speaking?

_____

2 Specific Vocabulary A C T

Worry means "to feel unhappy about something that might happen." What word in the same sentence means the opposite of *worry*?

_____

COLLABORATE

3 Talk About It

Compare how Nora and Danny feel about America. Justify your answer.

_____

"I don't want to ever leave Ireland," Danny said. "We won't have any friends in America. We'll be far away from Grandda, Paddy, and Colleen."

"Maybe you'll be glad it isn't Ireland," Nora said. "There will be enough food to eat. Mama and Da can **relax** and not **worry** so much. We'll all have a better life. America will be the land of our dreams."

Then Da carried a bag into the room. "Cheer up, my little loves! Why, in no time at all, you'll be joining me."

ELD.PI.3.1.Ex, ELD.PI.3.1.Br, ELD.PI.3.6.Ex, ELD.PI.3.6.Br See the California Standards section.

A year later, Da had saved enough money to send for his family. Mama, Danny, and Nora packed what little they had. They got on a **crowded** steamship and began their **voyage**.

The trip across the Atlantic Ocean was **rough**. The air inside the steamship smelled like a dirty sock. The ship tossed up and down for days. The waves were as big as mountains. Many **passengers** became seasick, but Nora and Danny felt fine.

Every day Nora daydreamed and reread Da's letters. She thought of the buildings and streetcars he wrote about. In her dreams, she could picture Da on a crowded street. He had a big smile on his face.

Tristan Elwell

ELD.PI.3.1.Ex, ELD.PI.3.1.Br, ELD.PI.3.6.Ex, ELD.PI.3.6.Br, ELD.PI.3.8.Ex, ELD.PI.3.8.Br, ELD.PII.3.2b.Ex, ELD.PII.3.2b.Br See the California Standards section.

1 Sentence Structure Ⓐ Ⓒ Ⓣ

Reread the first sentence in the first paragraph. When does Da send for his family? Circle the sentence part that tells you.

2 Specific Vocabulary Ⓐ Ⓒ Ⓣ

The word *rough* means "something is not easy and has many problems." Which clues in the second paragraph show why the trip is rough? Underline the clues.

COLLABORATE

3 Talk About It

Why does Nora feel fine during the rough voyage? Justify your answer.

_____

_____

1 Specific Vocabulary **A C T**

Look at the second sentence in the third paragraph. *Cheered* means "to shout when happy." Why does the crowd cheer?

_____

_____

2 Sentence Structure **A C T**

Reread the second sentence of the third paragraph. Circle the word *as*. It shows two actions are happening at the same time. What actions are happening at the same time? Underline the actions.

COLLABORATE

3 Talk About It

How does the crowd feel about the large statue?

_____

_____

One morning, Nora awoke. A moment later, she **realized** something was different. The ocean was as smooth as glass.

A few hours later, Nora, Danny, and Mama shivered together on the ship's deck. Snowflakes drifted through the air. Another traveler **noticed** and gave them a blanket. It was as thin as a rag, but nothing could have been more valuable to them.

Suddenly, someone shouted, "There's Lady Liberty!" As the ship passed the large statue, the crowd **cheered**. Someone shouted, "At last, we've arrived! We are in America." Soon, everyone was singing and dancing.

ELD.PI.3.1.Ex, ELD.PI.3.1.Br, ELD.PI.3.6.Ex, ELD.PI.3.6.Br, ELD.PI.3.8.Ex, ELD.PI.3.8.Br, ELD.PII.3.2b.Ex, ELD.PII.3.2b.Br See the California Standards section.

A ferry took the travelers to Ellis Island. In the main hall, doctors inspected the family. They looked for signs of illness. Mama had to answer many questions. Nora knew that people didn't get an opportunity, or another chance, to take these tests twice. Nora looked at Danny, then at Mama. They had to pass.

After a few hours, the family learned they could stay in America. As they filed off the ferry, Nora saw Uncle Sean's dark hair. Then she saw Da. His hands waved wildly. He had a big smile on his face. Dreams do come true, Nora thought as she waved back.

Make Connections

Why do Nora and her family immigrate to America? **ESSENTIAL QUESTION**

Did someone in your family move to a new place? How did they feel? **TEXT TO SELF**

Tristan Elwell

ELD.PI.3.1.Ex, ELD.PI.3.1.Br, ELD.PI.3.6.Ex, ELD.PI.3.6.Br, ELD.PII.3.1.Ex, ELD.PII.3.1.Br
See the California Standards section.

1 Sentence Structure Ⓐ Ⓒ Ⓣ

Read the fifth sentence of the first paragraph. Authors use commas to set apart a definition of a word. Circle the commas. Underline the definition of *opportunity*.

COLLABORATE

2 Talk About It

The family has to pass the doctors' tests on Ellis Island. Why are these tests so important?

_____

_____

_____

3 Comprehension Theme

Reread the last paragraph. Which sentence tells the author's message, or theme, of the story? Draw a box around the sentence.

Partner Discussion Work with a partner. Answer the questions. Discuss what you learned about "Sailing to America." Write the page numbers where you found text evidence.

Why do Nora and her family want to immigrate to America?

Text Evidence 🔍

I read that Da leaves for America to _____ . Page(s): _____

Nora thinks America is _____ , Page(s): _____

but Danny thinks _____ . Page(s): _____

How do Nora, Danny, and Mama feel when they arrive in America?

Text Evidence 🔍

The passengers on the boat cheer because _____ Page(s): _____

_____ .

Nora is worried at Ellis Island because _____ . Page(s): _____

When Nora sees Da, she thinks _____ . Page(s): _____

Group Discussion Present your answers to the group. Cite text evidence to justify your thinking. Listen to and discuss the group's opinions about your answers.

Write Work with a partner. Review your notes about "Sailing to America." Then write your answer to the Essential Question. Use text evidence to support your answer. Use vocabulary words from this week's reading in your writing.

Why do Nora and her family want to immigrate to America?

Mama and Da's dream is _____

_____.

Then Da goes to America because _____

_____.

Nora and her family come to America because _____

_____.

Nora sees Da in America and feels _____.

Share Writing Present your writing to the class. Discuss their opinions. Think about what the class has to say. Did they justify their claims? Explain why you agree or disagree with their claims.

I agree with _____.

That's a good comment, but _____.

Write to Sources

Rachel

Take Notes About the Text I took notes about the story. I used my notes to answer the question: *Was it a good idea for Nora and her family to immigrate to America? Tell why or why not. Use text evidence.*

I think it was a good idea.

Nora says Mama and Da will not worry.

In America, Da finds work and saves money.

The family will have enough food to eat.

Write About the Text I used my idea web to write about Nora's family immigrating to America.

Student Model: *Opinion*

I think it was a good idea for Nora and her family to immigrate to America on a steamship. Nora says that Mama will worry less. Da will worry less in America. The family will have enough food to eat. And Da finds work. I think that Nora's family makes the right choice to immigrate to America.

TALK ABOUT IT

Text Evidence

Circle the first sentence. What noun in this sentence tells how Nora's family traveled to America?

Grammar

Underline the sentence about Da finding work. How can you add the words *in America* to show where Da finds work?

Condense Ideas

Circle the sentences about worrying. How can you combine these sentences to connect the ideas?

Your Turn

Does the author do a good job of explaining why the family moves to America? Tell why or why not.

≫ *Go Digital*
Write your response online. Use your editing checklist.

TALK ABOUT IT

Weekly Concept Government

? Essential Question
How do people make government work?

>> *Go Digital*

112

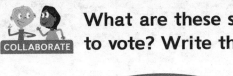

What are these students doing? Why is it important to vote? Write the words in the web.

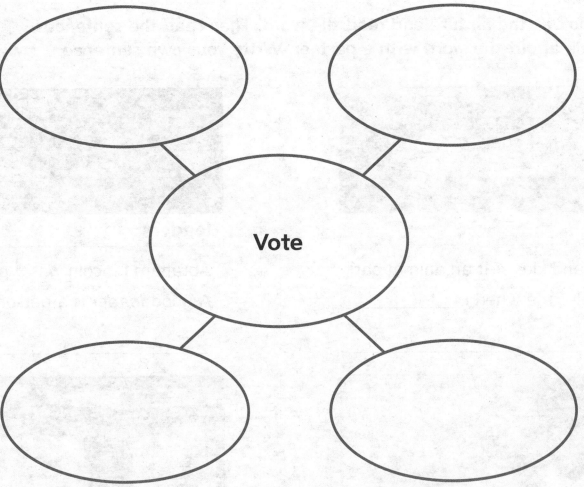

Vote

Discuss why people want to vote. Use the words from the web. You can say:

People want to vote because _____

_____.

People vote about _____.

Richard Hutchings/Corbis

More Vocabulary

Look at the picture and read the word. Then read the sentences.
Talk about the word with a partner. Write your own sentence.

adults

The **adults** and kids visit an animal park.

An *adult* helps me when I _____

_____.

leaders

Abraham Lincoln was a great **leader**.

A good *leader* is a person who _____

_____.

discuss

The students **discuss** the project.

I like to *discuss* _____

_____ with my friends.

power

Voters have the **power** to choose a president.

An election gives people *power* because

_____.

reason

We have a good **reason** to play outside.

One *reason* for playing outside is _____

_____.

results

Amber shows the **results** of her test.

The *results* of Amber's test show

_____.

Words and Phrases
Root words with *-ion*

Adding *-ion* to a verb makes it a noun.

The verb *elect* means "to choose."
We will <u>elect</u> a new class president.

The noun *election* means "voting for, or electing, someone."
We have an <u>election</u> for class president on Monday.

Read each sentence. Circle the verb in the first sentence. Then add *-ion* to the verb. Write the noun with *-ion* to complete the second sentence.

We elect a president every four years.

We vote in an _____.

I subtract in math.

I will use _____ to get the answer.

>> *Go Digital* **Add the verbs and nouns with *-ion* to your New Words notebook. Write a sentence using each word.**

COLLABORATE

1 Talk About It

Read the title. Discuss what you see. Write your ideas.

What is the meaning of the phrase "Every Vote Counts!"?

_____

_____

_____

_____

What are the students doing?

_____

_____

_____

_____

Take notes as you read the text.

Every VOTE Counts!

Essential Question

? **How do people make government work?**

Read about a group that teaches kids the power of voting.

Vote for the Class Pet

ELD.PI.3.1.Ex, ELD.PI.3.1.Br, ELD.PI.3.6.Ex, ELD.PI.3.6.Br See the California Standards section.

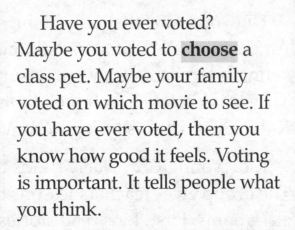

Have you ever voted? Maybe you voted to **choose** a class pet. Maybe your family voted on which movie to see. If you have ever voted, then you know how good it feels. Voting is important. It tells people what you think.

Many years ago, the **leaders** of our country wanted to know what people thought, too. They wrote a plan for our government. It is called the Constitution. It gives men and women in the United States the right to vote.

Each year, people who are eighteen years and older pick new leaders. They also vote on new laws. Voting gives Americans the **power** to choose.

1 **Specific Vocabulary** A C T

The word *choose* means "to decide which thing you want." Now read the first sentence in the last paragraph. What word means almost the same as *choose*?

_____

2 **Comprehension**
Author's Point of View

Reread the first paragraph. Which sentence tells the author's point of view about voting? Underline the sentence.

COLLABORATE

3 **Talk About It**

What did leaders of our country do many years ago?

_____

_____

ELD.PI.3.1.Ex, ELD.PI.3.1.Br, ELD.PI.3.6.Ex, ELD.PI.3.6.Br, ELD.PI.3.7.Ex, ELD.PI.3.7.Br
See the California Standards section.

117

TongRo Image Stock/Corbis

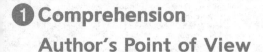

1 **Comprehension**

Author's Point of View

Reread the first paragraph. About how many Americans vote? Underline the words. What is the author's point of view about this fact?

_____

2 **Specific Vocabulary** A C T

Reread the last sentence in the last paragraph. What word in the sentence means the same as *elect*?

Who do kids learn to elect?

_____

COLLABORATE

3 **Talk About It**

How does Kids Voting USA help teachers and kids?

_____

Teaching Kids to Vote

Did you know that only about six out of every ten Americans vote? That's sad. Some people think that voting is too hard. They are unsure where to go to vote. They think it takes too much time. Now, a group called Kids Voting USA is trying to convince everyone to vote.

Kids Voting USA teaches kids that voting is important. The group gives teachers lessons to use in their classrooms. First, kids read stories and do fun activities about government. They also learn how to choose and **elect** a good leader.

Election Day is here!

First we sign in.

Richard Hutchings/Corbis

ELD.PI.3.1.Ex, ELD.PI.3.1.Br, ELD.PI.3.6.Ex, ELD.PI.3.6.Br, ELD.PI.3.7.Ex, ELD.PI.3.7.Br, ELD.PI.3.8.Ex, ELD.PI.3.8.Br See the California Standards section.

Next, kids talk with their families. They reread stories about candidates. These are the people who want to be chosen as leaders. Families **discuss** their ideas and make decisions. That way, when it's time to vote, kids know who they want to vote for.

On Election Day, kids get to vote just like **adults**. They use **ballots** like the ones in real elections. A ballot is a special form with the names of candidates on it. Kids mark their choices on the ballot. Then they put the ballot into a special box. Finally, all the votes are counted and recounted. The winners are announced, and everyone knows who won.

Then we mark a ballot.

BALLOT BOX

Finally we vote!

Richard Hutchings/Corbis

ELD.PI.3.1.Ex, ELD.PI.3.1.Br, ELD.PI.3.6.Ex, ELD.PI.3.6.Br, ELD.PI.3.10b.Ex, ELD.PI.3.10b.Br, ELD.PII.3.2b.Ex, ELD.PII.3.2b.Br See the California Standards section.

Text Evidence

1 Specific Vocabulary

Reread the second paragraph. A *ballot* is a piece of paper on which you mark your vote. What two things do kids do with a ballot? Underline the two things.

2 Sentence Structure A C T

Look at the fifth and sixth sentences in the last paragraph. Which sequence word connects the ideas in the sentences? Circle the word.

COLLABORATE

3 Talk About It

Discuss how Election Day is the same for adults and kids. Take notes. Then paraphrase what happens on the lines below.

_____

_____

_____

119

1 Sentence Structure A C T

Look at the last sentence of the first paragraph. Circle the comma that breaks the sentence into two parts. What will happen when these kids grow up? Draw a box around the sentence part that tells you.

2 Comprehension

Author's Point of View

Reread the last paragraph. In the author's opinion, what is exciting? Underline the sentence that tells you.

COLLABORATE

3 Talk About It

Why does the author think that learning to vote is important? Justify your answer.

_____

_____

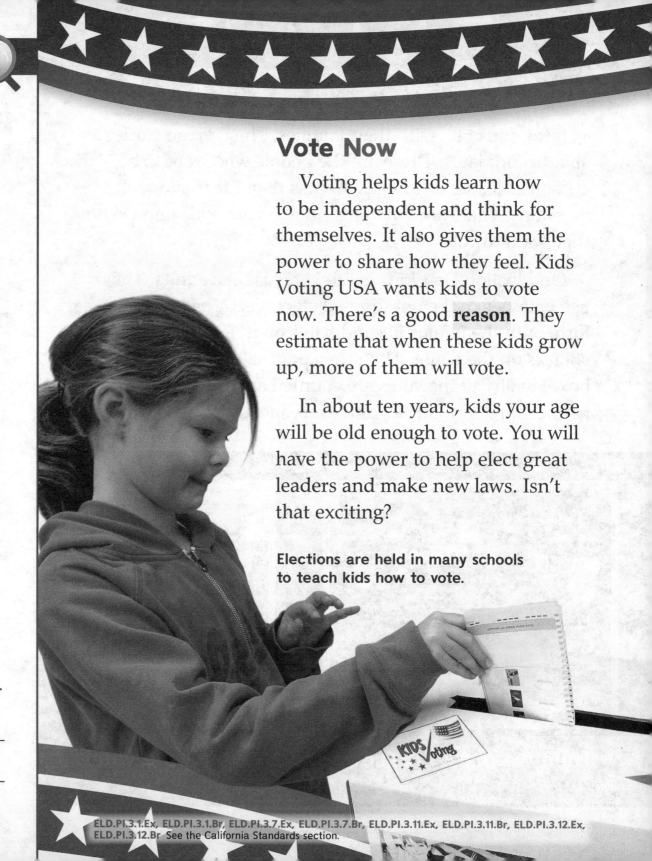

Vote Now

Voting helps kids learn how to be independent and think for themselves. It also gives them the power to share how they feel. Kids Voting USA wants kids to vote now. There's a good **reason**. They estimate that when these kids grow up, more of them will vote.

In about ten years, kids your age will be old enough to vote. You will have the power to help elect great leaders and make new laws. Isn't that exciting?

Elections are held in many schools to teach kids how to vote.

ELD.PI.3.1.Ex, ELD.PI.3.1.Br, ELD.PI.3.7.Ex, ELD.PI.3.7.Br, ELD.PI.3.11.Ex, ELD.PI.3.11.Br, ELD.PI.3.12.Ex, ELD.PI.3.12.Br See the California Standards section.

This bar graph shows the **results** of a class election. Which pet was the **favorite**?

Vote for a Class Pet

Hamster
Hermit Crab
Guinea Pig
Mouse

0 1 2 3 4 5 6 7 8

Make Connections

? How does voting give people the power to choose? **ESSENTIAL QUESTION**

Tell about a time when you voted. How did it make you feel? **TEXT TO SELF**

Text Evidence

1 Specific Vocabulary

Reread the paragraph. The word *favorite* means something you like best. Look at the bar graph. Circle the name of the favorite pet.

COLLABORATE

2 Talk About It

Look at the bar graph. Discuss why it is important for the class to vote for their favorite pet. Use text evidence and justify your ideas.

_____

_____

_____

_____

ELD.PI.3.1.Ex, ELD.PI.3.1.Br, ELD.PI.3.3.Ex, ELD.PI.3.3.Br, ELD.PI.3.11.Ex, ELD.PI.3.11.Br, ELD.PII.3.4.Ex, ELD.PII.3.4.Br See the California Standards section.

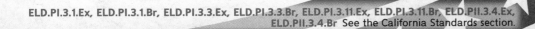

Respond to the Text

COLLABORATE

Partner Discussion Work with a partner. Answer the questions. Discuss what you learned about "Every Vote Counts!" Write the page numbers where you found text evidence.

Why do people in our country vote?

I read voting is important because _____.

According to the author, our country's leaders wanted _____

_____.

People vote for _____.

Text Evidence 🔍

Page(s): _____

Page(s): _____

Page(s): _____

How does Kids Voting USA teach kids to vote?

According to the author, Kids Voting USA _____

_____.

On Election Day, kids _____.

In ten years, Kids Voting USA wants _____.

Text Evidence 🔍

Page(s): _____

Page(s): _____

Page(s): _____

COLLABORATE

Group Discussion Present your answers to the group. Cite text evidence to justify your thinking. Listen to and discuss the group's opinions about your answers.

Write Work with a partner. Review your notes about "Every Vote Counts!" Then write your answer to the Essential Question. Use text evidence to support your answer. Use vocabulary words from this week's reading in your writing.

How can kids help make the United States government work?

Voting is important because _____

_____.

People vote for _____

_____.

Kids Voting USA helps _____

_____.

On Election Day, kids _____

_____.

Share Writing Present your writing to the class. Discuss their opinions. Think about what the class has to say. Did they justify their claims? Explain why you agree or disagree with their claims.

I agree with _____.

That's a good idea, but _____.

Write to Sources

pages 116–121

Take Notes About the Text I took notes on this idea web to answer the question: *In your opinion, does the author do a good job of showing people why they should vote? Think about the reasons the author gives.*

Marlon

The author says voting tells people what you think.

The author says voting gives people the power to choose.

The author does a good job of showing why people should vote.

The author says people can help elect leaders.

The author says people can help make new laws.

Write About the Text I used notes from my idea web to write an opinion.

Student Model: *Opinion*

I think the author does a good job of showing people why they should vote. The author gives several reasons. The author says that voting tells people what you think. Voting gives people the power to choose. People can help elect leaders. People can help make new laws. These are all good reasons to vote!

TALK ABOUT IT
COLLABORATE

Text Evidence

Circle an idea that comes from the notes. Why does Marlon use this idea as a supporting detail?

Grammar

Draw a box around the sentence that tells who people can elect. What adjective can you add to describe the noun *leaders*?

Condense Ideas

Underline the fifth and sixth sentences. How can you combine these sentences?

Your Turn
COLLABORATE

Do you agree or disagree with the author's opinion on voting? Use text details in your writing.

>> Go Digital
Write your response online. Use your editing checklist.

TALK ABOUT IT

? **Essential Question**
How can people help animals survive?

>> *Go Digital*

COLLABORATE

These manatees are threatened. They need our help. How can we help them survive? Write the words in the web.

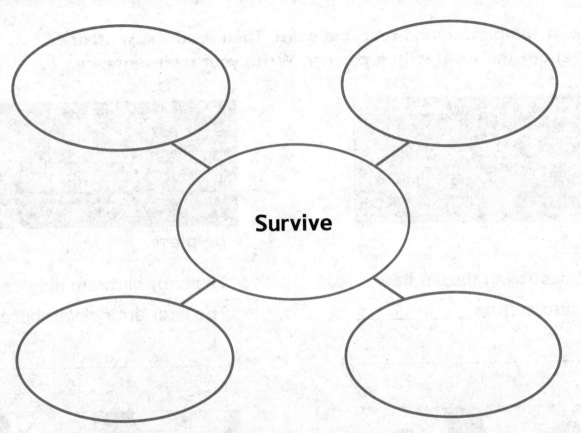

Survive

Discuss why it is important to help animals. How can people help animals survive? Use the words from the web. You can say:

It is important to _____ animals because

_____

People can _____

_____

_____.

More Vocabulary

Look at the picture and read the word. Then read the sentences. Talk about the word with a partner. Write your own sentence.

destroyed

A strong wind **destroyed** the big tree.

Strong storms also *destroy* _____

_____.

helpless

The baby birds are **helpless**.

The birds are *helpless* because _____

_____.

donations

We collected **donations** for our food drive.

People make *donations* to _____

_____.

heroes

The firefighters are Tom's **heroes**.

My favorite *heroes* are _____

because _____.

struggle

The baby **struggles** to walk.

The baby *struggles* because _____

_____.

supplies

We will take camping **supplies** on our hike.

Some useful school *supplies* are _____

_____.

Words and Phrases
Suffix *-er*

Add the suffix *-er* to an adjective. Then the suffix means "more."
small**er** = more small
The kitten is <u>small</u>, but the mouse is <u>smaller</u>.

Add the suffix *-er* to a verb. Then the suffix means "a person who does something."
paint**er** = a person who paints
The <u>painter</u> will <u>paint</u> our house.

Read the sentences below. Add *-er* to the underlined words. Complete the new sentences.

James feels <u>cold</u> without a coat.

James is _____ than Ted.

Miss Chang can <u>teach</u> many subjects.

Miss Chang is a good _____.

>> *Go Digital* **Add these words to your New Words notebook. Write sentences using each word with and without the suffix *-er*.**

COLLABORATE

1 Talk About It

Read the title. Discuss what you see. Write your ideas.

What does the title tell you?

_____

_____

_____

_____

What will the kids in the photo rescue?

_____

_____

_____

_____

Take notes as you read the text.

KIDS to the Rescue!

Olivia and Carter Ries,
founders of One More Generation

Essential Question

? How can people help animals survive?

Read how two children helped sea turtles survive an oil spill.

ELD.PI.3.1.Ex, ELD.PI.3.1.Br, ELD.PI.3.6.Ex, ELD.PI.3.6.Br See the California Standards section.

Courtesy of One More Generation

What a mess! There was dark, **gooey** oil everywhere. It slid across the water. It coated rocks and sand. It made swimming hard for sharks and dolphins. The oil spill in the Gulf of Mexico was making animals sick and **helpless**.

Two kids from a small town in Georgia watched the news. They saw pictures of sea turtles coated with oil. They watched animals **struggle** to move. As a result, they decided it was time to do something. The animals in the gulf needed two super **heroes** to help them!

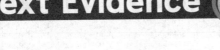

Text Evidence

1 Comprehension

Author's Point of View

Reread the first paragraph. What does the author think about the oil spill? Underline the sentence that shows the author's point of view.

2 Specific Vocabulary Ⓐ Ⓒ Ⓣ

Reread the second sentence. Something that is gooey is thick and sticky. Underline words that give clues to the meaning of *gooey*.

COLLABORATE

3 Talk About It

Why did two kids decide to help animals in the Gulf of Mexico?

_____

_____

_____

ELD.PI.3.1.Ex, ELD.PI.3.1.Br, ELD.PI.3.6.Ex, ELD.PI.3.6.Br, ELD.PI.3.7.Ex, ELD.PI.3.7.Br
See the California Standards section.

131

Text Evidence

1 Sentence Structure (A)(C)(T)

The second sentence in the first paragraph has two parts. The word *that* connects the two parts. What does Olivia and Carter's group do? Underline the part of the sentence that tells you.

COLLABORATE

2 Talk About It

Why did Olivia and Carter name their group One More Generation?

_____

_____

_____

3 Specific Vocabulary (A)(C)(T)

Read the fifth sentence in the last paragraph. An endangered animal may die out or become extinct. Underline two clues that show why the Kemp's ridley turtle is endangered.

132

Olivia and Carter to the Rescue!

Meet Olivia and Carter Ries. They started a group that works to save animals. Olivia was seven years old, and Carter, her brother, was eight-and-a-half. They named their group One More Generation. They want animals to be around for kids in the future.

Olivia and Carter believe everyone can make a difference. They are sending an important message. Their message is that everyone can help animals.

Olivia and Carter watched oil spread for miles across the gulf. More and more animals were getting sick. The Kemp's ridley turtle was one of them. There are only a few thousand left in the world. They are **endangered**, and their population is getting smaller and smaller. The oil threatened to ruin their homes and their habitat.

Olivia and Carter Ries learned how oil harms Kemp's ridley turtles.

One More Generation

ELD.PI.3.1.Ex, ELD.PI.3.1.Br, ELD.PI.3.6.Ex, ELD.PI.3.6.Br, ELD.PI.3.12.Ex, ELD.PI.3.12.Br See the California Standards section.

This female turtle is clean and healthy. It is being returned to the gulf.

Steven Senne/AP Images

Oil Spoils Everything

Olivia and Carter learned that the female turtles were swimming across the gulf to Mexico. They were going to lay eggs on the beaches there. But the thick oil **destroyed** the resources the turtles need to live. The harmful oil covered the sand. It made it hard for them to swim.

Sea turtles survive by eating seaweed, jellyfish, and small sea animals. The oil spill **spoiled** their food, too. Without food, the turtles die.

ELD.PI.3.1.Ex, ELD.PI.3.1.Br, ELD.PI.3.6.Ex, ELD.PI.3.6.Br, ELD.PI.3.7.Ex, ELD.PI.3.7.Br
See the California Standards section.

Text Evidence

1 **Sentence Structure** Ⓐ Ⓒ Ⓣ

Reread the second sentence. The word *there* refers back to the location in the first sentence. Circle the location *there* refers to.

2 **Specific Vocabulary** Ⓐ Ⓒ Ⓣ

Look at the last paragraph. Something that is *spoiled* is damaged or hurt in some way. What was spoiled by the oil spill?

_____

_____

COLLABORATE

3 **Talk About It**

Why does this section have the title "Oil Spoils Everything"?

Justify your answer. _____

_____

133

Text Evidence

1 Sentence Structure A C T

Reread the sixth sentence in the first paragraph. Circle the commas. Underline the name of each group in the series.

2 Comprehension

Author's Point of View

Reread the last paragraph. What is the author's point of view about Olivia and Carter's plan? Draw a box around the sentence that tells you. Which details support the point of view? Circle the sentences.

COLLABORATE

3 Talk About It

What did Olivia and Carter do with the supplies they collected?

_____

_____

Saving the Sea Turtles

Olivia and Carter recognized how big the problem was. The turtles needed help. First they made a thoughtful plan. Then they called a rescue group in New Orleans. They found out that the workers needed useful cleaning **supplies** and wipes. Next the kids asked friends, relatives, and people in their town to help. They told them how the **donations** would help remove oil from the turtles.

Olivia and Carter collected supplies for four months. They rode with their parents to New Orleans. They carried the supplies with them. Then the kids watched caretakers clean hundreds of sea turtles. With the help of many people, the turtles were soon spotless. Olivia and Carter's plan worked. It was a huge success!

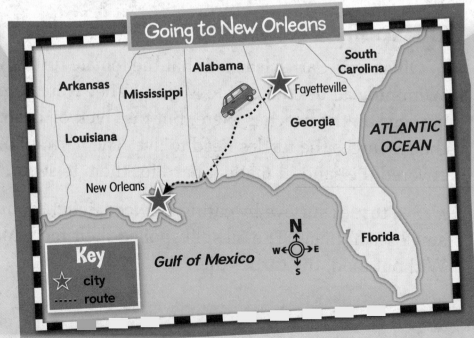

Going to New Orleans

South Carolina
Alabama
Arkansas
Mississippi Fayetteville
Georgia
ATLANTIC OCEAN
Louisiana
New Orleans
N
W — E
S
Florida
Key
☆ city
----- route
Gulf of Mexico

TSI Graphics

ELD.PI.3.1.Ex, ELD.PI.3.1.Br, ELD.PI.3.6.Ex, ELD.PI.3.6.Br, ELD.PI.3.7.Ex, ELD.PI.3.7.Br, ELD.PII.3.2a.Ex, ELD.PII.3.2a.Br See the California Standards section.

Keeping Busy

Olivia and Carter work with many other groups to help animals all over the world. They give talks at museums and schools. They ask **community** leaders to support laws that help animals. They help rescue animals in danger.

Olivia and Carter are truly super heroes to endangered animals. With their help, many animals will survive for one more generation.

Ways You Can Help Animals!

- Protect animal nests.
- Pick up trash at parks and wild places.
- Keep water clean.
- Stop using plastic bags.

Carter and his mom unpack supplies in New Orleans.

Make Connections

? Describe the steps that Olivia and Carter took to help the Kemp's ridley sea turtles. ESSENTIAL QUESTION

What can you and your friends do to help animals? TEXT TO SELF

Text Evidence 🔍

1 Specific Vocabulary A⬤T

Reread the first paragraph. A *community* is a group of people who live in the same area. Look at the second sentence. Circle two things you can find in a community.

2 Sentence Structure A⬤T

Reread the last sentence. Circle the comma that breaks the sentence into two parts. Read each part. What will allow many animals to survive? Underline the sentence part that tells you.

COLLABORATE

3 Talk About It

Discuss different ways to help animals survive. Write one way you can help animals.

_____

_____

_____

ELD.PI.3.1.Ex, ELD.PI.3.1.Br, ELD.PI.3.6.Ex, ELD.PI.3.6.Br See the California Standards section.

135

Respond to the Text

Partner Discussion Work with a partner. Answer the questions. Discuss what you learned about "Kids to the Rescue!" Write the page numbers where you found text evidence.

What happened in the Gulf of Mexico?

Text Evidence

I read that an oil spill _____. Page(s): _____

Based on the text, animals in the gulf _____. Page(s): _____

According to the author, sea turtles _____. Page(s): _____

How did Olivia and Carter help sea turtles survive?

Text Evidence

Olivia and Carter wanted to _____. Page(s): _____

The kids started a group _____. Page(s): _____

I read that they _____ and went to _____. Page(s): _____

Now Olivia and Carter are helping _____. Page(s): _____

COLLABORATE

Group Discussion Present your answers to the group. Cite text evidence to justify your thinking. Listen to and discuss the group's opinions about your answers.

COLLABORATE

Write Work with a partner. Review your notes about "Kids to the Rescue!" Then write your answer to the Essential Question. Use text evidence to support your answer. Use vocabulary words from this week's reading in your writing.

How did Olivia and Carter help animals survive?

During the oil spill, Olivia and Carter _____

_____.

They started a group _____.

Olivia and Carter took supplies to _____

_____.

Now sea turtles _____.

COLLABORATE

Share Writing Present your writing to the class. Discuss their opinions. Think about what the class has to say. Did they justify their claims? Explain why you agree or disagree with their claims. You can say:

I think your idea is _____.

I do not agree with you because _____.

Write to Sources

Rhett

Take Notes About the Text I took notes on this idea web to answer the question: *What were the effects of the oil spill on the turtles?*

KIDS to the Rescue!

pages 130–135

The oil slid across the water. Then it coated the sand.

It was hard for the turtles to swim.

Effects of the oil spill on the turtles

The oil destroyed the resources turtles need.

The oil spoiled the turtles' food.

Write About the Text I used my idea web to write about the effects of the oil spill on the turtles.

Student Model: *Informative Text*

The oil spill had harmful effects on the turtles. The turtles lived in the Gulf of Mexico. First, the oil slid across the water. Then it coated the sand. The oil made it hard for the turtles to swim. The oil destroyed the resources the turtles need to live. It spoiled the turtles' food. Some of the turtles died without food. The oil spill hurt the turtles.

TALK ABOUT IT

Text Evidence

Draw a box around the third and fourth sentences. Why did Rhett use the words *first* and *then* in these sentences?

Grammar

Circle a past tense verb. Why did Rhett use past tense to write about the oil spill?

Condense Ideas

Underline the two sentences about resources and food. How can you combine these sentences to connect the ideas?

Your Turn

Think about what Olivia and Carter do. Write a paragraph describing Olivia and Carter.

>> *Go Digital*
Write your response online. Use your editing checklist.

ELD.PI.3.10a.Ex, ELD.PI.3.10a.Br, ELD.PI.3.10b.Ex, ELD.PI.3.10b.Br, ELD.PII.3.2b.Ex, ELD.PII.3.2b.Br, ELD.PII.3.3.Ex, ELD.PII.3.3.Br, ELD.PII.3.7.Ex, ELD.PII.3.7.Br

See the California Standards section. 139

TALK ABOUT IT

Weekly Concept Figure It Out

? **Essential Question**
How do people
figure things out?

>> *Go Digital*

COLLABORATE

What is this boy doing? How can the family figure out where to go? Write the words in the web.

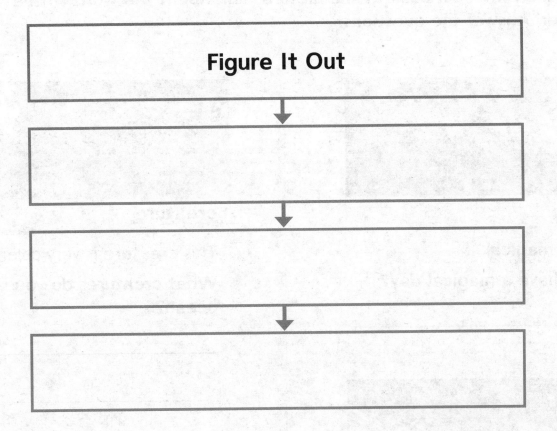

Figure It Out

Discuss ways that you figure things out. Use the words from the web. You can say:

To figure something out, I _____,

_____, and

_____.

More Vocabulary

COLLABORATE

Read the sentence. Look at the picture. Talk about the word with a partner. Answer the questions.

magical

The sunset was **magical**.

When did you have a magical day?

_____.

creature

This **creature** is very colorful.

What creatures do you see in the ocean?

_____

_____.

rumbling

The storm was **rumbling** loudly.

What do you hear rumbling?

_____.

142 ELD.PI.3.1.Ex, ELD.PI.3.1.Br, ELD.PI.3.5.Ex, ELD.PI.3.5.Br, ELD.PI.3.12.Ex, ELD.PI.3.12.Br See the California Standards section.

Poetry Terms

alliteration

Alliteration is the same sound at the beginning of several words.

Becky **b**ounces a **b**asketball.

rhyme

The words *bear* and *pear* **rhyme**. The words end in the same sound.

I saw a little b**ear**.
It ate a yellow p**ear**.

simile

A **simile** compares two different things. It uses the words *like* or *as*.

My **brother** sleeps <u>like</u> a **log**.

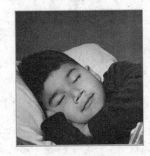 

① Comprehension
Point of View

Look at the picture. Reread the first four lines of the poem. How does the narrator feel about Abuelita's empanadas? Underline the details that tell you.

② Literary Element
Alliteration

Reread the third line. What words begin with the same sound? Underline the words.

③ Sentence Structure Ⓐ🅒🅣

Read the sixth and seventh line. Circle the punctuation marks that show someone is speaking. Who is speaking? Circle the name.

Empanada Day

One bite of Abuelita's empanadas
And my mouth purrs like a cat.
 "Teach me," I beg and bounce on my feet,
 "Teach me to make this **magical** treat."
Abuelita smiles,
 "Be an observer, watch and learn,
Then you too can take a turn."

Essential Question

? **How do people figure things out?**

Read poems about different ways to figure things out.

Dara Goldman

ELD.PI.3.1.Ex, ELD.PI.3.1.Br, ELD.PI.3.7.Ex, ELD.PI.3.7.Br, ELD.PII.3.2a.Ex, ELD.PII.3.2a.Br
See the California Standards section.

She sets before me a ball of dough,
Round and golden as the sun.
My eyes wide as saucers, I watch and follow,
    Press circles flat as pancakes,
    Spoon on apple slices and nose-tickling spices,
    Seal it all in, a half-moon envelope of **bliss**.
Together we write down every step
As the empanadas bake and crisp in the oven,
My stomach **rumbling** like a hungry bear.

                    Ah, empanada day!

                                    — George Santiago

ELD.PI.3.1.Ex, ELD.PI.3.1.Br, ELD.PI.3.7.Ex, ELD.PI.3.7.Br, ELD.PII.3.6.Ex, ELD.PII.3.6.Br
See the California Standards section.

145

Text Evidence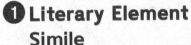

❶ Literary Element
Simile

Reread the fourth line. What does the poet compare the flat dough to? Circle the word.

❷ Specific Vocabulary 🅐🅒🅣

Reread the sixth line. *Bliss* is a very happy feeling. Why does the boy feel bliss?

_____

_____

COLLABORATE

❸ Talk About It

Reread the last two lines of the poem. Discuss how the boy feels about the empanadas. Write your reasons.

_____

_____

1 **Literary Element**
Rhyme

Read the first two lines of "Cold Feet." Circle the words that rhyme. Write the word in the last line that rhymes with these words.

_____

COLLABORATE

2 **Talk About It**

Reread "Cold Feet." Discuss why the inventor knits socks. Underline the words that give clues to your reason. Write a reason.

_____

_____

3 **Comprehension**
Point of View

How does the narrator of "Our Washing Machine" feel about the machine? Circle the words.

Cold Feet

An inventor with feet like ice,

And toes like ten shivering mice,

Looked at clothes, studied feet.

Read about cold and heat,

And knit the first socks, warm and nice.

OUR WASHING MACHINE

Our washing machine is a bear

That munches up socks by the pair.

He will suds them and grumble

As they spin, turn, and tumble,

Then spit them out, ready to wear.

Dara Goldman

ELD.PI.3.1.Ex, ELD.PI.3.1.Br, ELD.PI.3.6.Ex, ELD.PI.3.6.Br, ELD.PI.3.7.Ex, ELD.PI.3.7.Br, ELD.PI.3.8.Ex, ELD.PI.3.8.Br See the California Standards section.

Bugged

A creature has crawled on my knee,

It's a bug green and round as a pea.

His five wings are fish fins,

He's got teeth sharp as pins.

Just imagine him chomping on me!

I read every bug book I see,

To learn what this **creature** might be.

I ask scientists too,

But they don't have a clue.

So I'm **bugged** by this great mystery.

Make Connections

? What are different ways to figure things out? Talk about what happens in each poem.
ESSENTIAL QUESTION

Which poem has the best way to solve a problem? TEXT TO SELF

ELD.PI.3.1.Ex, ELD.PI.3.1.Br, ELD.PI.3.6.Ex, ELD.PI.3.6.Br, ELD.PI.3.7.Ex, ELD.PI.3.7.Br
See the California Standards section.

Text Evidence

1 **Specific Vocabulary** **ACT**

Reread the title and the last line. The verb *bug* means "to bother or annoy someone." What is bugging the narrator?

2 **Literary Element Rhyme**

Reread the sixth and seventh lines of the poem. Which two words rhyme? Circle the two words. Now read the last line. Write the word that rhymes with these two words.

3 **Comprehension Point of View**

Reread the last five lines of "Bugged." What is the narrator's point of view about the creature? Underline the details that show her point of view.

147

Respond to the Text

Partner Discussion Work with a partner. Answer the questions. Discuss what you learned about "Empanada Day." Write the page numbers where you found text evidence.

What does the boy want to learn how to do?

Text Evidence 🔍

In the first two lines, the boy describes _____ .

Page(s): _____

_____ .

The boy wants Abuelita to _____

Page(s): _____

_____ .

How does the boy learn to make empanadas?

Text Evidence 🔍

First, the boy watches _____ .

Page(s): _____

Next, Abuelita and the boy _____ .

Page(s): _____

Finally, they write _____ .

Page(s): _____

COLLABORATE

Group Discussion Present your answers to the group. Cite text evidence to justify your thinking. Listen to and discuss the group's opinions about your answers.

Write Work with a partner. Review your notes about "Empanada Day." Then write your answer to the Essential Question. Use text evidence to support your answer. Use vocabulary words from this week's reading in your writing.

> **How does the boy figure out how to make empanadas?**
>
> The boy wants Abuelita to _____
>
> _____.
>
> Abuelita says _____.
>
> The boy watches _____
>
> _____.
>
> Together Abuelita and the boy _____
>
> _____.

Share Writing Present your writing to the class. Discuss their opinions. Think about what the class has to say. Did they justify their claims? Explain why you agree or disagree with their claims.

I agree with your ideas _____.

I do not agree with your ideas because _____.

Write to Sources

pages 144–147

Sophia

Take Notes About the Text I took notes about the poems on this chart to answer the question: *How do the poets use alliteration in the poems "Empanada Day" and "Bugged"?*

Name of Poem	Examples of Alliteration
"Empanada Day"	I <u>beg</u> and <u>bounce</u> on my feet Then you <u>too</u> can <u>take</u> a <u>turn</u>
"Bugged"	A <u>creature</u> has <u>crawled</u> on my knee His <u>five</u> wings are <u>fish</u> <u>fins</u>

Write About the Text I used my chart to write a paragraph about how the poets use alliteration.

Student Model: *Informative Text*

The poet of "Empanada Day" uses alliteration in the words "beg" and "bounce." These words begin with the letter *b*. The words "too," "take," and "turn" also begin with the same sound. The poet of "Bugged" uses alliteration, too. He uses alliteration in the words "creature" and "crawled." He also writes "His five wings are fish fins." The words "five" and "fish" start with the letter *f*. The word "fins" starts with the letter *f*. There are examples of alliteration in "Empanada Day" and "Bugged."

TALK ABOUT IT

Text Evidence
Circle the complete line that comes from the poem "Bugged." Why does Sophia use this line as evidence?

Grammar
Draw a box around the last sentence. How can you add the word *many* to describe the examples?

Condense Ideas
Underline the sentences about the words *fish* and *fins*. How can you combine these sentences to connect the ideas?

Your Turn

How do the poets use similes? Use text evidence in your writing.

>> Go Digital
Write your response online. Use your editing checklist.

ELD.PI.3.1.Ex, ELD.PI.3.1.Br, ELD.PI.3.10a.Ex, ELD.PI.3.10a.Br, ELD.PI.3.10b.Ex, ELD.PI.3.10b.Br, ELD.PII.3.4.Ex, ELD.PII.3.4.Br, ELD.PII.3.7.Ex, ELD.PII.3.7.Br
See the California Standards section.

Unit 3

One of a Kind

∽ THE ∽
BIG IDEA

Why are individual qualities important?

Weekly Concept Be Unique

Essential Question

What makes different animals unique?

>> *Go Digital*

COLLABORATE

How are dolphins unique? Write things that make dolphins unique in the web. Describe how dolphins are different from other animals.

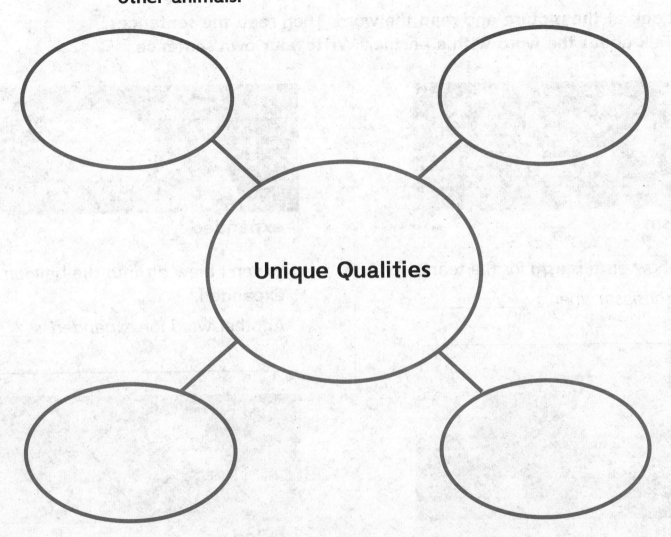

Unique Qualities

Discuss how a dolphin's unique qualities help it survive. Use the words from the chart. You can say:

A dolphin's _____ are _____.

They help a dolphin _____.

More Vocabulary

COLLABORATE

Look at the picture and read the word. Then read the sentences. Talk about the word with a partner. Write your own sentence.

enthusiasm

The fans show **enthusiasm** for the team.

I show *enthusiasm* when _____

_____.

expanded

When I blew air into the balloon, it **expanded**.

Another word for *expanded* is _____

_____.

exhausted

Ben is **exhausted** after the game.

I feel *exhausted* after I _____.

failed

The player **failed** to catch the ball.

The word *failed* means _____.

rescued

Tomás **rescued** his cat.

Another word for *rescued* is _____ .

volunteered

The girls **volunteered** to build the house.

I want to *volunteer* to _____

_____ .

Words and Phrases
Prefixes

The prefix *un-* means "not."
unable = not able
I am **<u>unable</u>** to play after school.

The prefix *re-* means "again."
replays = plays again
Tito **<u>replays</u>** his favorite song.

Read the sentences below. Write the word that means the same as the underlined words.

My sister is <u>not able</u> to tie her shoes.

My sister is _____ to tie her shoes.

My class <u>reads</u> the poem <u>again</u>.

My class _____ the poem.

>> *Go Digital* **Add these words with prefixes to your New Words notebook. Write a sentence to show the meaning of each word.**

COLLABORATE

1 Talk About It

Look at the illustration. Read the title. Discuss what you see. Write your ideas.

What does the title tell you?

_____

_____

_____

Who is in the illustration?

_____

_____

Where are they?

_____

_____

Take notes as you read the story.

THE INCHWORM'S TALE

Essential Question

?

What makes different animals unique?

Read about how one animal uses its special features to solve a problem.

ELD.PI.3.1.Ex, ELD.PI.3.1.Br, ELD.PI.3.6.Ex, ELD.PI.3.6.Br See the California Standards section.

Long ago, Anant and his sister, Anika, went swimming. They swam all afternoon and became very tired. They were **exhausted** and climbed onto a large, flat rock to rest. Soon they fell asleep.

A strange and **mysterious** thing happened as they slept. The rock beneath them grew and **expanded** until it reached the clouds.

Anant awoke and looked around. "Sister, wake up!" he cried in disbelief. "Am I dreaming, or are we among the clouds?"

Anika rubbed her eyes. "You're not dreaming, brother. This rock has grown while we slept!" The children looked around and saw fabulous blue sky and wonderful white clouds.

The children were so high, Anika felt dizzy. Anant searched for a way to climb down, but he could not find a path. Anant and Anika started to cry. They felt fear and dismay.

ELD.PI.3.1.Ex, ELD.PI.3.1.Br, ELD.PI.3.6.Ex, ELD.PI.3.6.Br, ELD.PI.3.7.Ex, ELD.PI.3.7.Br
See the California Standards section.

Text Evidence

❶ Specific Vocabulary Ⓐ Ⓒ Ⓣ

The word *mysterious* means "hard to understand or explain." Underline the words that tell what is mysterious.

❷ Sentence Structure Ⓐ Ⓒ Ⓣ

Reread the third paragraph. Draw a box around the pronouns *he* and *we*. Circle the noun that *he* refers to. Write the nouns that *we* refers to.

_____

❸ Comprehension

Problem and Solution

Reread the fourth and fifth paragraphs. What is the problem in the story? How do Anant and Anika feel about the problem? Justify your answer.

_____

_____

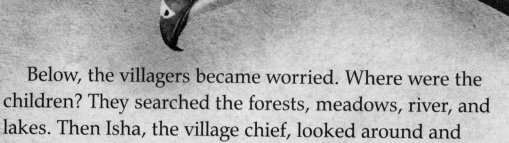

1 **Sentence Structure** **A C T**

Reread the first sentence in the second paragraph. Underline the pronoun *he*. Who does the pronoun *he* refer to? Draw a box around the name.

2 **Specific Vocabulary** **A C T**

Look at the word *squinted*. *Squint* means "squeeze the eyes together." Why does Hawk squint? Underline the words that tell you.

3 **Comprehension**

Problem and Solution

Reread the last paragraph. Why does Hawk gather food and leaves for the children?

_____

_____

_____

Below, the villagers became worried. Where were the children? They searched the forests, meadows, river, and lakes. Then Isha, the village chief, looked around and noticed Hawk sitting on a tree branch.

"Hawk, will you help us find Anant and Anika?" he asked. "You have sharp, watchful eyes and strong wings. They are your best features. Please use them to help us find the children."

Hawk agreed to help and flew up into the sky. He tilted his head and **squinted** his eyes at the bright sunlight. When he was near the clouds, he spied the children on the rock.

"Don't be afraid," said Hawk. "We will **rescue** you!"

Hawk was unable to carry the children down the rock, so he gathered lots of food for them to eat. Then he brought large leaves to keep them warm. Hawk wanted to make sure they were safe and unharmed.

ELD.PI.3.6.Ex, ELD.PI.3.6.Br See the California Standards section.

Hawk flew down to the village and spoke to Isha. Isha called all the animals together and told them they needed help to get the children down. He asked each animal to use its most **special** feature to climb the tall rock. Several tried and **failed**.

Mouse's teeth were strong and unique, but they couldn't help her climb up the rock.

Bear's huge claws were good for climbing up trees. However, they could not help him scale rocks.

Mountain Lion's claws were sharp and powerful, but the rock was too slippery and he slid back down.

Finally, a tiny voice filled with **enthusiasm** spoke up and offered to help. "May I try, please? It's me, Too-Tock, the Inchworm!"

ELD.PI.3.1.Ex, ELD.PI.3.1.Br, ELD.PI.3.6.Ex, ELD.PI.3.6.Br See the California Standards section.

1 Comprehension

Problem and Solution

Reread the first paragraph. What is Isha's solution to the children's problem? Underline the solution.

2 Specific Vocabulary A C T

The word *special* means "different in some way." Circle the special features of Mouse, Bear, and Mountain Lion in the next three paragraphs.

COLLABORATE

3 Talk About It

How does Inchworm feel about helping? Write your ideas. Cite text evidence.

_____

_____

_____

_____

1 Sentence Structure Ⓐ Ⓒ Ⓣ

Adjectives describe people, places, and things. Reread the first paragraph. Circle the adjective that describes the mountain.

2 Comprehension

Problem and Solution

Reread the second paragraph. What steps do Hawk and Inchworm take to solve the problem? Underline the sentences that show the steps.

COLLABORATE

3 Talk About It

Why is Inchworm the best animal to help the children? Cite two pieces of text evidence.

_____

_____

_____

Inchworm showed them all how skillful she was at climbing. Hawk **volunteered** to carry Inchworm to the top of the rock. Then she could lead Anant and Anika down the giant mountain. Isha agreed to the plan.

So Hawk carefully picked up Inchworm in his beak. Together they flew to the top of the rock where the children were waiting. Along the way, Inchworm planned for the trip down.

ELD.PI.3.1.Ex, ELD.PI.3.1.Br, ELD.PI.3.6.Ex, ELD.PI.3.6.Br, ELD.PI.3.7.Ex, ELD.PI.3.7.Br
See the California Standards section.

It took almost a week for the three to climb down to the village. **Inch by inch**, Inchworm led the children carefully down the rocky slope. Every day, Hawk brought food to the children. Every day he reappeared in the village with news for the villagers.

Finally, Inchworm, Anant, and Anika reached the bottom of the rock. Everyone cheered and called Inchworm a hero. It was a glorious, splendid day.

"From this day on," said Isha, "I rename the big rock, Too-Tock-Awn-oo-Lah, after the brave inchworm."

Text Evidence

1 Specific Vocabulary A C T

Reread the second sentence in the first paragraph. The phrase *inch by inch* means "very slowly." What does Inchworm do "inch by inch"? Underline the words that tell you.

2 Sentence Structure A C T

Reread the last sentence in the first paragraph. When does Hawk reappear? Draw a box around the words that tell you. Where does Hawk reappear? Circle the words that tell you.

COLLABORATE

3 Talk About It

Why does Isha name the rock after Inchworm? Justify your answer.

_____

_____

Make Connections

? What unique feature does Inchworm have? How does it help? ESSENTIAL QUESTION

What do your special features help you do? TEXT TO SELF

Jago Silver

ELD.PI.3.1.Ex, ELD.PI.3.1.Br, ELD.PI.3.3.Ex, ELD.PI.3.3.Br, ELD.PI.3.6.Ex, ELD.PI.3.6.Br, ELD.PI.3.12.Ex, ELD.PI.3.12.Br See the California Standards section.

Respond to the Text

COLLABORATE

Partner Discussion Work with a partner. Answer the questions. Discuss what you learned about "The Inchworm's Tale." Write the page numbers where you found text evidence.

What are Inchworm and Hawk's unique features?

Text Evidence 🔍

Hawk has _____. Page(s): _____

Hawk also has _____. Page(s): _____

Inchworm is _____. Page(s): _____

How do Hawk and Inchworm solve the problem in the story?

Text Evidence 🔍

First, Hawk searches and _____. Page(s): _____

Then Hawk carries _____. Page(s): _____

Inchworm leads _____. Page(s): _____

COLLABORATE

Group Discussion Present your answers to the group. Cite text evidence to justify your thinking. Listen to and discuss the group's opinions about your answers. You can say:

I think your ideas _____.

Write Work with a partner. Review your notes about "The Inchworm's Tale." Then write your answer to the Essential Question. Use text evidence to support your answer. Use vocabulary words from this week's reading in your writing.

How do Inchworm and Hawk's unique features help them solve a problem?

Hawk and Inchworm use their features to _____.

First, Hawk uses his _____

to _____.

Then Hawk _____.

Inchworm helps by using her _____

to _____

_____.

Share Writing Present your writing to the class. Discuss their opinions. Think about what the class has to say. Did they justify their claims? Explain why you agree or disagree with their claims. You can say:

I agree with _____, and I think _____.

That's a good comment, but _____.

ELD.PI.3.1.Ex, ELD.PI.3.1.Br, ELD.PI.3.3.Ex, ELD.PI.3.3.Br, ELD.PI.3.5.Ex, ELD.PI.3.5.Br, ELD.PI.3.6.Ex, ELD.PI.3.6.Br, ELD.PI.3.9.Ex, ELD.PI.3.9.Br
See the California Standards section.

pages 158-163

Nya

Take Notes About the Text I took notes about the story on this chart to respond to the prompt: *Add a paragraph to the story. Describe what the children say to Inchworm after they get to the bottom of the rock.*

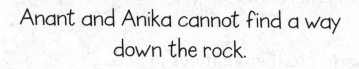

Anant and Anika cannot find a way down the rock.

↓

They feel afraid.

↓

Inchworm leads the children down the rock to the village.

↓

Everyone cheers. Inchworm is a hero.

Write About the Text I used notes from my chart
to write a paragraph that tells what the children
say to Inchworm.

Student Model: *Narrative Text*

Anant and Anika thanked Inchworm.

"We are happy to be home!" said Anant.

"You are our hero," added Anika. "How

can we thank you?"

Inchworm said, "I am very hungry, and

I would like some leaves to eat."

The children found some leaves. They

found the leaves in the forest. Then they

gave the leaves to Inchworm. Inchworm

smiled and ate the leaves.

TALK ABOUT IT

Text Evidence

Draw a box around what Anant says.
Why does Nya use an exclamation mark?

Grammar

Underline the sentence that tells the first
thing Anant and Anika do. What is the
verb in this sentence?

Condense Ideas

Circle the sentences about finding leaves.
How can you condense the sentences?

Your Turn

Add another paragraph to the
story. Tell what happens when
Mouse tries to climb the rock.

>> Go Digital
Write your response online. Use your editing checklist.

Jackie Robinson was a leader. What makes a good leader? Write qualities of good leaders in the web. Describe how leaders change the way people think.

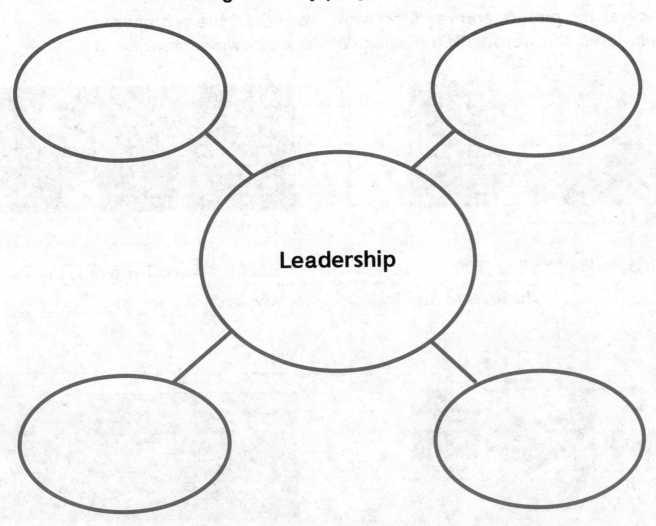

Leadership

Discuss how these qualities help a leader like Jackie Robinson. Use the words from the chart. You can say:

A good _____ is _____ and _____.

These qualities help a leader to _____.

ELD.PI.3.1.Ex, ELD.PI.3.1.Br, ELD.PI.3.12.Ex, ELD.PI.3.12.Br, ELD.PII.3.3.Ex, ELD.PII.3.3.Br, ELD.PII.3.4.Ex, ELD.PII.3.4.Br See the California Standards section.

More Vocabulary

COLLABORATE

Look at the picture and read the word. Then read the sentences. Talk about the word with a partner. Write your own sentence.

belonged to

The two fish **belonged to** Eve.

_____ *belongs to* me.

favorite

Hector's **favorite** color is blue.

My *favorite* color is _____.

extended

The skater **extended** her leg.

I *extend* my arm to _____

_____.

insisted

Mom **insisted** that Emma wear a helmet.

The word *insisted* means _____

_____.

neighbor

Jim talked to his **neighbor**.

My *neighbor* is _____

_____.

prove

The footprints **prove** that an animal was here.

The word *prove* means _____

_____.

Words and Phrases
Cause-and-Effect Words

Cause-and-effect words connect two ideas.

The word *so* shows what happened.
What happened when you were hot?
I was hot, <u>so</u> I went to the beach.

The word *because* tells why something happened.
Why did Marco drink water?
Marco drank water <u>because</u> he was thirsty.

Underline the cause-and-effect word in each sentence.

Pam was tired so she went to bed.

Ben stayed home because he was sick.

Write your own sentences using *so* and *because*.

_____

_____

_____

>> Go Digital Add the cause-and-effect words *so* and *because* to your New Words notebook. Include the sentences you wrote.

(t)Blend Images/Moxie Productions/Getty Images; (b)Edoma/iStock/360/Getty Images

1 Talk About It

Look at the illustration. Read the title. Discuss what you see. Write your ideas.

What does the title tell you about Jane?

_____

_____

_____

What does the illustration show? Where and when does the story take place?

_____

_____

_____

Take notes as you read the story.

Jane's Discovery

Essential Question

? How can one person change the way you think?

Read how a future president changed Jane's life.

ELD.PI.3.1.Ex, ELD.PI.3.1.Br, ELD.PI.3.6.Ex, ELD.PI.3.6.Br See the California Standards section.

Jane slammed the door of the log cabin and raced **toward** the Indiana woods. Mother and Father **insisted** that Jane go to school and learn to read. It was September of 1825, and Jane wanted to help on the farm like her brothers. Therefore, she told her parents "No!" and refused to learn to read.

Jane scooped up her long skirts and splashed through a small stream. Running helped her collect her thoughts, so she ran for what seemed like hours. She dashed around a tree and wasn't paying attention. As a result, she tripped over a pair of long legs stretched out in the grass.

The legs **belonged to** her **neighbor**, Abe Lincoln. Abe was leaning against a tree reading a book. He smiled, stood up, and **extended** his arm to help Jane up.

Peter Ferguson

ELD.PI.3.1.Ex, ELD.PI.3.1.Br, ELD.PI.3.6.Ex, ELD.PI.3.6.Br, ELD.PI.3.7.Ex, ELD.PI.3.7.Br, ELD.PII.3.2b.Ex, ELD.PII.3.2b.Br See the California Standards section.

Text Evidence

❶ Specific Vocabulary Ⓐ Ⓒ Ⓣ

The word *toward* shows someone is moving in the direction of something. Underline the words that tell what Jane races toward.

❷ Sentence Structure Ⓐ Ⓒ Ⓣ

Reread the second sentence in the first paragraph. Circle the word *that*. It connects the two parts of the sentence. Underline what happens in the first part. Box what happens in the second part.

❸ Comprehension
Cause and Effect

Reread the second paragraph. What causes Jane to trip over a pair of long legs? Write the cause.

_____

1 Sentence Structure **A C T**

Reread the first sentence. Circle the word that connects the two parts of the sentence. Then underline the action in each part.

2 Specific Vocabulary **A C T**

Look at the word *spare*. It means "extra or not used." What does Abe do in his spare time? Write the words below.

_____

3 Comprehension

Cause and Effect

Reread the last paragraph. Which word shows that there is a cause and an effect? Circle the word. Write the cause and the effect.

Cause: _____

Effect: _____

Jane recognized Abe and knew what a hard-worker he was. But she also heard he was not like the other sixteen-year-old boys in Perry County. Abe was different because he spent all of his **spare** time reading books.

"Why are you running so fast?" Abe asked. "Are you hurt?"

Jane frowned. "No, I'm all right," she said. "I'm running because I'm upset. My parents want me to learn to read, and I told them no!"

ELD.PI.3.1.Ex, ELD.PI.3.1.Br, ELD.PI.3.6.Ex, ELD.PI.3.6.Br, ELD.PI.3.7.Ex, ELD.PI.3.7.Br, ELD.PII.3.2b.Ex, ELD.PII.3.2b.Br See the California Standards section.

Abe looked down at his book and then at Jane.

"Reading can change your life," he said quietly. "Meet me here tomorrow, and I'll **prove** to you how important reading is."

Jane met Abe the next afternoon. He showed her a book about George Washington. One of his **favorite** teachers had donated it to him, and he had read it many times.

Abe began to read aloud while Jane listened carefully. He read about Washington and what a great leader he was. He read about Washington's **courage** and bravery.

"Someday I want to be as courageous as George Washington," said Abe proudly. "Someday I will be president of the United States, too."

"I believe you will make a great president," said Jane. "Look at what a good leader you are now. You've completely changed my mind about reading!"

Abe smiled. "Tell your parents you will learn to read," he said. "Then meet me here every day after school. We will read together, and I will help you."

ELD.PI.3.1.Ex, ELD.PI.3.1.Br, ELD.PI.3.6.Ex, ELD.PI.3.6.Br, ELD.PII.3.4.Ex, ELD.PII.3.4.Br
See the California Standards section.

Text Evidence

1 Specific Vocabulary ACT

Reread the fourth paragraph. What does *courage* mean? Underline the word in the sentence that gives you a clue. Write the meaning.

_____

2 Sentence Structure ACT

An adjective describes a noun. Reread the second sentence of the fourth paragraph. What kind of leader was George Washington? Underline the adjective that tells you.

COLLABORATE

3 Talk About It

Why does Jane think Abe will make a great president? Write your ideas. Justify your answer.

_____

_____

_____

175

Text Evidence

At first, Jane was nervous and uncertain about learning to read, but she met Abe every day like clockwork. Fortunately, Jane's intense **dislike** for reading was only a temporary feeling. She was getting the hang of it. As a result, her nervousness began to disappear. One afternoon, Abe surprised her. To her amazement, he gave her his favorite book.

Peter Ferguson

"Thank you," she said. "Now that I can read, I don't ever want to stop."

Years later, Jane opened her **newspaper** and read the good news. Her friend, Abe Lincoln, had been elected president of the United States. She smiled and thought about the day she tripped over his long legs. That was the day that changed her life.

PERRY COUNTY TRIBUNE

Lincoln Elected!

Abe Lincoln Elected 16th President

November 6, 1860

Illinois Senator Abraham Lincoln was elected 16th president of the United States of America. He defeated three other candidates in the November 1860 election.

Make Connections

? How does Abe change Jane's life? ESSENTIAL QUESTION

Who has helped change the way you think? TEXT TO SELF

Text Evidence

1 Sentence Structure **A C T**

Look at the first sentence in the first paragraph. Circle the pronoun. Put a box around the name of the character.

2 Specific Vocabulary

Write the two small words in the compound word *newspaper*.

_____

COLLABORATE

3 Talk About It

Why does Jane think about the day she tripped over Abe's legs? Why is this day important to her? Justify your answer.

_____

_____

_____

ELD.PI.3.1.Ex, ELD.PI.3.1.Br, ELD.PI.3.6.Ex, ELD.PI.3.6.Br See the California Standards section.

Respond to the Text

Partner Discussion Work with a partner. Answer the questions. Discuss what you learned about "Jane's Discovery." Write the page numbers where you found text evidence.

How does Jane feel about learning to read at first?

At first, Jane _____.

Text Evidence 🔍

Page(s): _____

Instead, she wants to _____.

Page(s): _____

Jane runs into _____ because she _____.

Page(s): _____

How does Abe help Jane enjoy reading?

Text Evidence 🔍

Abe loves _____ and shows Jane _____.

Page(s): _____

Then Abe teaches _____.

Page(s): _____

Years later, Jane reads _____.

Page(s): _____

Jane thinks Abe Lincoln _____.

Page(s): _____

Group Discussion Present your answers to the group. Cite text evidence to justify your thinking. Discuss the group's opinions about your answers.

Write Work with a partner. Review your notes about "Jane's Discovery." Then write your answer to the Essential Question. Use text evidence to support your answer. Use vocabulary words from this week's reading in your writing.

How does Abe change the way Jane thinks?

Jane does not want to _____.

Then she runs into _____

_____.

Abe shows Jane _____ and teaches her _____

_____

Years later, Jane reads _____.

Jane thinks about how _____.

Share Writing Present your writing to the class. Discuss their opinions. Think about what the class has to say. Did they justify their claims? Explain why you agree or disagree with their claims.

I agree with _____.

That's a good comment, but _____.

Write to Sources

pages 172–177

Isabella

Take Notes About the Text I took notes about the story to respond to the prompt: *Think about when Jane reads that Abe is elected president. Write a thank you letter that Jane writes. Use details from the story.*

> Jane tells Abe she does not want to learn to read.

⬇

> Abe helps Jane learn to read.

⬇

> Abe gives Jane a book about George Washington.

⬇

> Years later, Jane reads in a newspaper that Abe is elected president.

Write About the Text I used notes from my chart to write a letter to Abe from Jane.

Student Model: *Narrative Text*

Dear Abe,

    I am happy because you were elected president of the United States. I read it in the newspaper.

    I still have the book you gave me about George Washington. I remember how you helped me learn to read. Thank you for teaching me. You taught me how to read. It changed my life.

                    Your friend,

                    Jane

TALK ABOUT IT

COLLABORATE

Text Evidence

Underline a sentence that comes from the notes. Why does Isabella use this information in the story?

Grammar

Draw a box around the verb *remember*. Why does Isabella use present tense here?

Condense Ideas

Circle the sentences about Abe teaching Jane. How can you condense them?

Your Turn

COLLABORATE

Write a letter from Abe to a friend. Have Abe talk about Jane. Use details from the story.

>> *Go Digital*
Write your response online. Use your editing checklist.

ELD.PI.3.10a.Ex, ELD.PI.3.10a.Br, ELD.PI.3.10b.Ex, ELD.PI.3.10b.Br, ELD.PII.3.1.Ex, ELD.PII.3.1.Br, ELD.PII.3.3.Ex, ELD.PII.3.3.Br, ELD.PII.3.7.Ex, ELD.PII.3.7.Br
See the California Standards section.

? **Essential Question**

What do we know about Earth and its neighbors?

>> *Go Digital*

What objects can you see in the sky? Write these objects in the web. Talk about the time of day you see these objects.

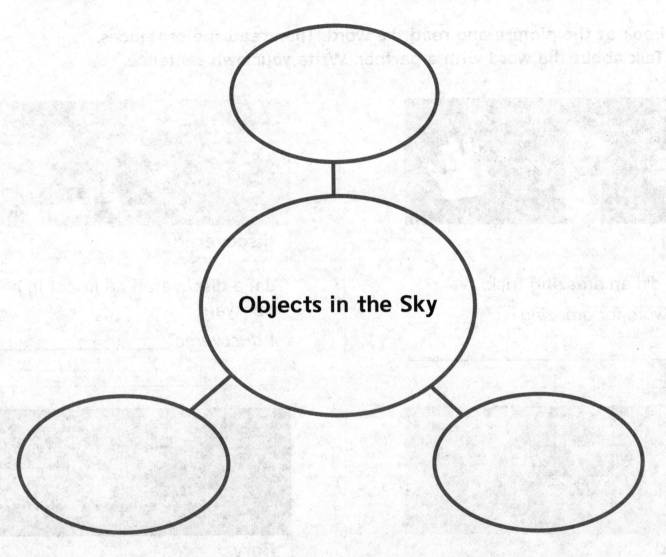

Objects in the Sky

Discuss whether the things in the sky are close to Earth or far from it. Use the words from the chart. You can say:

The _____ is _____ Earth.

The _____ are _____ Earth.

ELD.PI.3.1.Ex, ELD.PI.3.1.Br, ELD.PI.3.2.Ex, ELD.PI.3.2.Br, ELD.PII.3.5.Ex, ELD.PII.3.5.Br See the California Standards section.

More Vocabulary

COLLABORATE Look at the picture and read the word. Then read the sentences. Talk about the word with a partner. Write your own sentence.

amazing

The man did an **amazing** trick.

Another word for *amazing* is _____

_____ .

discovered

Jane **discovered** an insect in her backyard.

I *discovered* _____

_____ .

collected

Ben **collected** shells at the beach.

I like to *collect* _____

_____ .

fiery

We saw a **fiery** sunset.

The word *fiery* means _____

_____ .

gigantic

The elephant is **gigantic**.

Another word for *gigantic* is _____

_____ .

information

The class finds **information** on the Internet.

I find *information* _____

_____ .

Words and Phrases
Possessive Nouns and Contractions

An apostrophe and *s* (*'s*) shows ownership.
tree's = belongs to the tree
The <u>tree's</u> *leaves are green.*

An apostrophe in a contraction stands for the missing letter.
that's = that is
<u>That's</u> *a big insect.*

Write the word that means the same as the underlined words in the sentence.

The red shirt <u>belongs to the boy</u>.

The _____ shirt is red.

<u>That is</u> my favorite song.

_____ my favorite song.

>> Go Digital Add the contractions and possessive nouns to your New Words notebook. Write a sentence to show the meaning of each.

1 Talk About It

Look at the illustration. Read the title. Discuss what you see. Write your ideas.

What is the topic of the article?

_____

_____

_____

_____

Who is in the illustration? What is he looking at?

_____

_____

_____

_____

Take notes as you read the text.

Earth
and Its Neighbors

Essential Question

What do we know about Earth and its neighbors?

Read about how we have learned about space.

Galileo studied the sky with a telescope he built.

ELD.PI.3.1.Ex, ELD.PI.3.1.Br, ELD.PI.3.6.Ex, ELD.PI.3.6.Br See the California Standards section.

If the Sun could talk, it might say, "Look at me! Look at my sunspots! I am so hot!" Without the Sun, Earth would be a cold, dark planet. How do we know this?

Thanks to the **astronomer** Galileo, we know a lot about the Sun and the rest of our solar system.

Telescopes: Looking Up

Galileo did not invent the telescope. However, 400 years ago he did build one that was strong enough to study the sky. When Galileo looked into space, he saw the rocky surface of the Moon. When he looked at the Sun, he **discovered** spots on its **fiery** surface.

The Moon is Earth's closest neighbor.

Text Evidence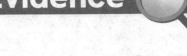

1 **Specific Vocabulary** Ⓐ Ⓒ Ⓣ

Look at the second paragraph. An *astronomer* is a scientist who studies the planets and stars. Circle the name of the astronomer.

2 **Sentence Structure** Ⓐ Ⓒ Ⓣ

Reread the second paragraph. The comma breaks the sentence into two parts. Why do we know a lot about the solar system? Underline the sentence part that tells you.

3 **Comprehension**

Main Idea and Details

Reread the third paragraph. What did Galileo's telescope help him to do? Write the key details.

_____

_____

_____

ELD.PI.3.1.Ex, ELD.PI.3.1.Br, ELD.PI.3.6.Ex, ELD.PI.3.6.Br See the California Standards section.

187

Text Evidence

1 Specific Vocabulary A C T

Look at the word *launched*. In this sentence, the word *launched* means "sent into the sky." What did scientists launch? Write the word.

_____

2 Comprehension

Main Idea and Key Details

Reread the third paragraph. What did satellites do when they circled the globe? Draw a box around two key details about satellites in this paragraph.

3 Sentence Structure A C T

Reread the third sentence in the fourth paragraph. It is a compound sentence. Circle the word that connects the two clauses. What were satellites doing in space? Underline the clause.

Astronomy, or the study of space, began with the simple telescope. But astronomers wanted to look at the sky more closely. They made bigger telescopes that could see further than the one Galileo used. Astronomers still had many questions.

Satellites: A Step Closer

In 1958, scientists **launched** Explorer 1, the first American satellite, into space. It was an exciting day for America.

Soon many satellites circled the globe and took photographs of Earth, the Moon, stars, and other planets. They **collected** a large amount of **information**. Satellites even tracked the temperature on the planet Saturn.

Scientists have learned many things about the solar system from satellites. That's why they kept sending more into space. Soon there were hundreds of satellites in space making **amazing** discoveries, but astronomers wanted to know even more. That's why they found a way to put a man on the Moon.

Explorer 1 takes off.

ELD.PI.3.1.Ex, ELD.PI.3.1.Br, ELD.PI.3.6.Ex, ELD.PI.3.6.Br, ELD.PII.3.2b.Ex, ELD.PII.3.2b.Br
See the California Standards section.

One Giant Leap

In 1961, Alan Shepard became America's first astronaut. He blasted off into space in a rocket and then turned around and came back to Earth. His short trip was a big success. Shepard's flight proved that people could go into space.

After Shepard, more astronauts went into space. Some **orbited** the Earth. Some walked on the dusty, bumpy surface of the Moon. They took pictures and collected Moon rocks. Astronauts wanted to answer some important questions. Did the Sun's warmth heat the Moon? Could the Moon support life someday?

Astronaut Edwin "Buzz" Aldrin walks toward the Lunar Module. Aldrin left his footprints on the Moon.

Aldrin brought home this Moon rock.

ELD.PI.3.1.Ex, ELD.PI.3.1.Br, ELD.PI.3.6.Ex, ELD.PI.3.6.Br, ELD.PII.3.1.Ex, ELD.PII.3.1.Br
See the California Standards section.

Text Evidence

1 Comprehension

Main Idea and Details

Reread the first paragraph. Why was astronaut Alan Shepard an important astronaut? Underline three key details about him.

2 Specific Vocabulary ACT

The word *orbited* means "traveled in a circle around something." Who orbited the Earth after Shepard?

_____

_____

COLLABORATE

3 Talk About It

What did other astronauts do in space? Take notes. Paraphrase what you learned on the lines below.

_____

_____

Text Evidence

1 Sentence Structure ⒶⒸⓉ

The first sentence in the first paragraph has two clauses. The word *that* connects the two clauses. What did the astronauts bring back? Circle the phrase that tells you.

2 Specific Vocabulary ⒶⒸⓉ

The word *fascinating* means "very interesting." Underline an example of fascinating information that the Hubble sends to Earth.

COLLABORATE

3 Talk About It

How has the Hubble helped scientists learn about space?

_____

_____

_____

_____

Scientists studied the photographs and Moon rocks that the astronauts brought back. They made exciting discoveries using telescopes and satellites. But it wasn't enough. Scientists wanted to get closer to the other planets. Soon they found a way!

Hubble and Beyond

Scientists created another telescope, but this time it was **gigantic**. They sent it up into space. The Hubble Space Telescope was launched in 1990. It's still up there and orbits the Earth above the clouds. It takes clear, close-up photographs of stars and planets. It sends **fascinating** information back to Earth. The Hubble helps scientists study Earth and its neighbors. It also helps astronomers see planets outside our solar system.

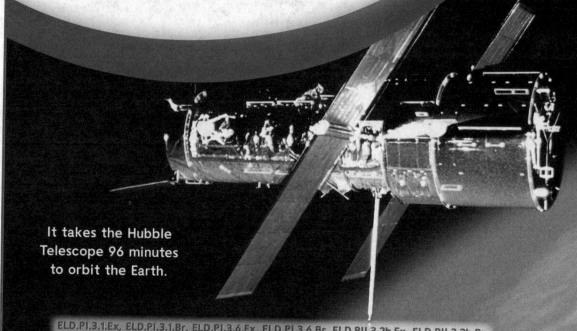

It takes the Hubble Telescope 96 minutes to orbit the Earth.

Frank Whitney/The Image Bank/Getty Images

ELD.PI.3.1.Ex, ELD.PI.3.1.Br, ELD.PI.3.6.Ex, ELD.PI.3.6.Br, ELD.PII.3.2b.Ex, ELD.PII.3.2b.Br
See the California Standards section.

More Discoveries Every Day

Scientists are still asking questions about Earth and its neighbors in space. With the help of satellites, telescopes, and astronauts, they will continue to explore and find answers.

What Can We See?

With Our Eyes	With a Simple Telescope	With the Hubble Telescope
The Moon	Craters on the Moon	Planets outside our solar system
The Sun	Sunspots	Stars bigger than the Sun and far, far away
Mars	Clouds around Jupiter	Jupiter's surface

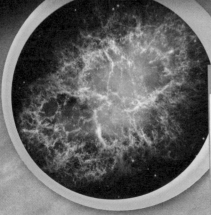

This is a Hubble Telescope photo of an exploding star.

Make Connections

How have we learned about Earth and its neighbors in space? ESSENTIAL QUESTION

What do you see when you look at the sky? TEXT TO SELF

1 Comprehension

How will scientists find answers about space? Underline the sentence that tells you.

2 Sentence Structure A C T

Reread the last sentence in the paragraph. Circle the pronoun. Who does the pronoun refer to? Write the word.

_____

COLLABORATE

3 Talk About It

Discuss the chart "What Can We See?" Compare what we see with our eyes and with the Hubble. Write your ideas.

_____

_____

_____

ELD.PI.3.1.Ex, ELD.PI.3.1.Br, ELD.PI.3.6.Ex, ELD.PI.3.6.Br, ELD.PII.3.2a.Ex, ELD.PII.3.2a.Br
See the California Standards section.

Respond to the Text

Partner Discussion Work with a partner. Answer the questions. Discuss what you learned about "Earth and Its Neighbors." Write the page numbers where you found text evidence.

What tools do we use to learn about space?

We use telescopes to _____.

We send satellites into space to _____.

We send astronauts into space to _____.

Text Evidence 🔍

Page(s): _____

Page(s): _____

Page(s): _____

How does the Hubble Telescope help us learn about space?

The Hubble Telescope orbits the _____.

It takes clear photographs of _____.

Then it sends the information _____.

Text Evidence 🔍

Page(s): _____

Page(s): _____

Page(s): _____

COLLABORATE

Group Discussion Present your answers to the group. Cite text evidence to justify your thinking. Listen to and discuss the group's opinions about your answers. You can say:

I think your ideas _____.

COLLABORATE

Write Work with a partner. Review your notes about "Earth and Its Neighbors." Then write your answer to the Essential Question. Use text evidence to support your answer. Use vocabulary words from this week's reading in your writing.

How do we learn about Earth and its neighbors?

Long ago, astronomers used telescopes _____.

Then scientists sent satellites _____.

Satellites collected _____
_____.

Astronauts _____.

Scientists invented the Hubble Telescope _____.

It helps us learn about _____.

COLLABORATE

Share Writing Present your writing to the class. Discuss their opinions. Think about what the class has to say. Did they justify their claims? Explain why you agree or disagree with their claims.

I agree with your ideas about _____.

That's a good comment, but _____.

ELD.PI.3.1.Ex, ELD.PI.3.1.Br, ELD.PI.3.3.Ex, ELD.PI.3.3.Br, ELD.PI.3.5.Ex, ELD.PI.3.5.Br, ELD.PI.3.6.Ex, ELD.PI.3.6.Br, ELD.PI.3.9.Ex, ELD.PI.3.9.Br

See the California Standards section. 193

Write to Sources

pages 186–191

Take Notes About the Text I took notes about the text to answer the question: *How have scientists learned about the solar system?*

Noah

> Galileo made a strong telescope 400 years ago.

> Astronomers made bigger telescopes.

> America's first astronaut went into space in 1961.

> The Hubble Space Telescope takes photographs and sends information to Earth.

ELD.PI.3.6.Ex, ELD.PI.3.6.Br See the California Standards section.

monkeybusinessimages/iStock/360/Getty Images

Write About the Text I used my notes to write a paragraph about scientists and the solar system.

Student Model: *Informative Text*

Scientists began to study the solar system long ago. First, Galileo made a strong telescope 400 years ago. Then astronomers made bigger telescopes.

Later, people went into space. America's first astronaut went into space in 1961. Then astronauts walked on the Moon.

Today, the Hubble Space Telescope takes photographs in space. It sends information back to Earth. Scientists continue to learn more about space.

TALK ABOUT IT

COLLABORATE

Text Evidence

Draw a box around a sentence from the notes. Why does Noah use this information as a supporting detail?

Grammar

Underline a past-tense verb in the second paragraph. Why does Noah use past-tense verbs to write about these events?

Condense Ideas

Circle the sentences about the Hubble Telescope. How can you combine these sentences?

COLLABORATE

Your Turn

Why did astronauts go to the Moon? What did they do on the Moon? Use details from the text in your answer.

>> Go Digital
Write your response online. Use your editing checklist.

COLLABORATE What is the boy learning about in the picture? What can people learn from nature? Write ideas about nature in the web. Describe how humans use the ideas from nature to make new things.

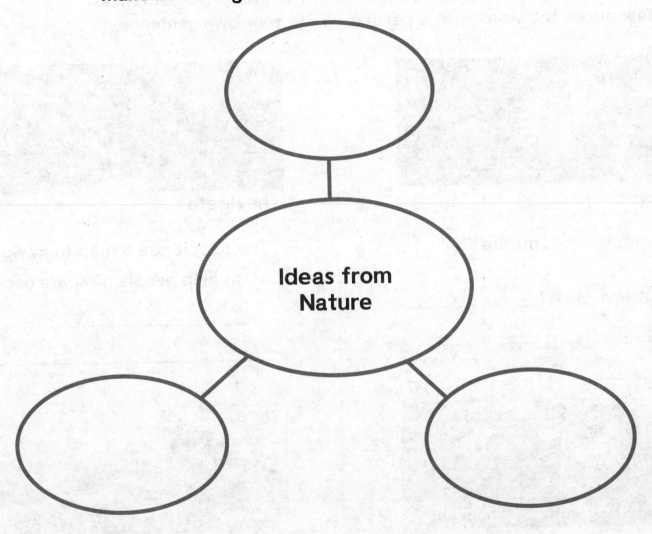

Ideas from Nature

Discuss inventions inspired by things from nature. Use the words from the chart. You can say:

A _____ inspired scientists to make _____.

More Vocabulary

COLLABORATE

Look at the picture and read the word. Then read the sentences. Talk about the word with a partner. Write your own sentence.

inspiration

The photographer gets **inspiration** from trees.

I find *inspiration* when I _____

_____.

locate

I need to **locate** my lost car keys.

Another word for *locate* is _____

_____.

navigate

The people use a map to **navigate**.

Maps help people *navigate* because

_____

_____.

objects

I see many **objects** on the desk.

Some *objects* in my backpack are _____

_____.

ELD.PI.3.1.Ex, ELD.PI.3.1.Br, ELD.PI.3.5.Ex, ELD.PI.3.5.Br, ELD.PI.3.12.Ex, ELD.PI.3.12.Br See the California Standards section.

observations

Lena makes **observations** about nature.

I make *observations* when _____

_____ .

ordinary

The boys wear **ordinary** white shirts.

The word *ordinary* means _____

_____ .

Words and Phrases
Suffix *-ion*

Add the suffix *-ion* to a verb to make it a noun.

discuss + -ion = *discussion*
We had a <u>discussion</u> about the stars.

invent + -ion = *invention*
The telephone was an important <u>invention</u>.

Circle the word with the suffix *-ion*.

We use subtraction in mathematics.

I added the cards to my collection.

Write your own sentences using *subtraction* and *collection*.

_____

_____

_____

_____

>> Go Digital Add the words with the suffix **-ion to your New Words notebook. Write your sentences with the words in your notebook.**

COLLABORATE

1 Talk About It

Read the title. Discuss what you see. Write your ideas.

What does the title tell you?

_____

_____

_____

_____

Who do you see on page 201?

_____

_____

_____

What is he doing?

_____

_____

Take notes as you read the text.

BATS DID IT FIRST

Essential Question

? **What ideas do we get from nature?**

Read about how bats inspired a new cane for blind people.

ELD.PI.3.1.Ex, ELD.PI.3.1.Br, ELD.PI.3.6.Ex, ELD.PI.3.6.Br See the California Standards section.

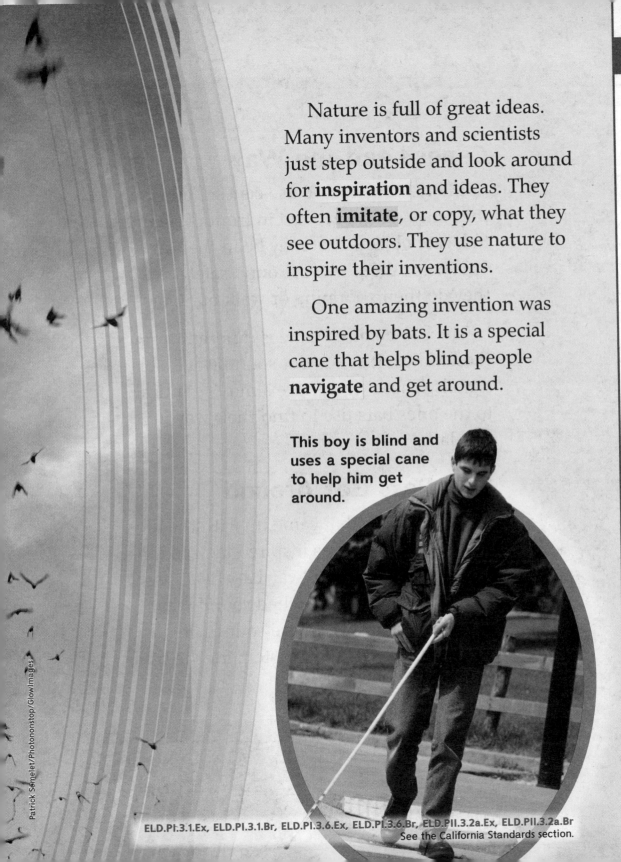

Nature is full of great ideas. Many inventors and scientists just step outside and look around for **inspiration** and ideas. They often **imitate**, or copy, what they see outdoors. They use nature to inspire their inventions.

One amazing invention was inspired by bats. It is a special cane that helps blind people **navigate** and get around.

This boy is blind and uses a special cane to help him get around.

ELD.PI.3.1.Ex, ELD.PI.3.1.Br, ELD.PI.3.6.Ex, ELD.PI.3.6.Br, ELD.PII.3.2a.Ex, ELD.PII.3.2a.Br
See the California Standards section.

Text Evidence

1 Specific Vocabulary Ⓐ Ⓒ Ⓣ

Look at the third sentence in the first paragraph. What context clue shows the meaning of *imitate*? Circle the word.

2 Comprehension

Main Idea and Key Details

Reread the first paragraph. Where do inventors and scientists get ideas? Underline the key details that support this main idea.

3 Sentence Structure Ⓐ Ⓒ Ⓣ

Reread the last paragraph. Circle the pronoun in the second sentence. Which noun does the pronoun refer to? Write the noun.

Text Evidence

1 Sentence Structure ACT

Look at the last sentence in the first paragraph. The word *as* connects two parts of the sentence. It shows two things happening at the same time. When do canes help blind people move safely? Underline the sentence part that tells you.

2 Specific Vocabulary ACT

The word *bat-inspired* means "an idea that came from bats." What object is bat-inspired? Circle the word.

3 Comprehension

Main Idea and Key Details

Reread the last paragraph. How did the scientist think of an idea for a new cane? Write a detail that supports this main idea.

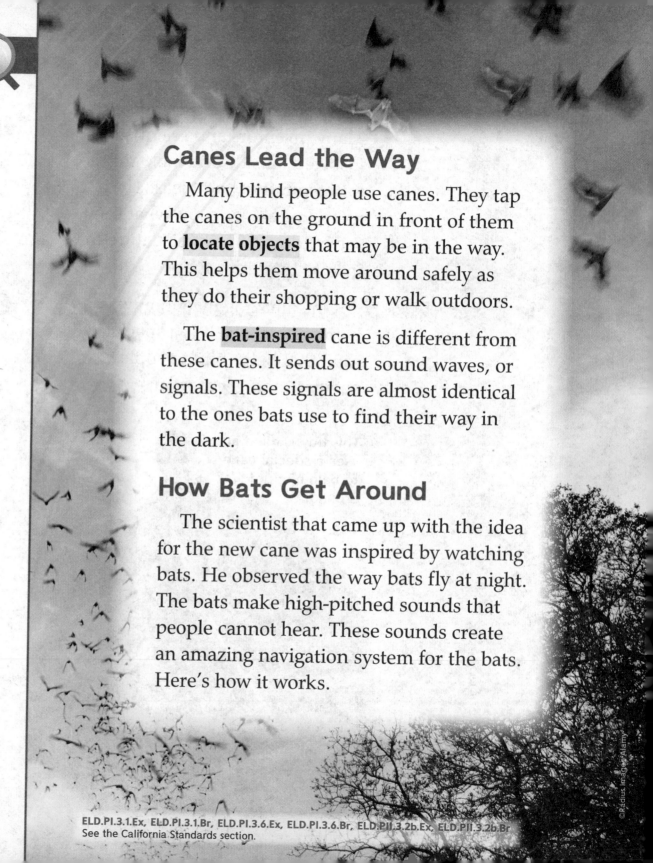

Canes Lead the Way

Many blind people use canes. They tap the canes on the ground in front of them to **locate objects** that may be in the way. This helps them move around safely as they do their shopping or walk outdoors.

The **bat-inspired** cane is different from these canes. It sends out sound waves, or signals. These signals are almost identical to the ones bats use to find their way in the dark.

How Bats Get Around

The scientist that came up with the idea for the new cane was inspired by watching bats. He observed the way bats fly at night. The bats make high-pitched sounds that people cannot hear. These sounds create an amazing navigation system for the bats. Here's how it works.

ELD.PI.3.1.Ex, ELD.PI.3.1.Br, ELD.PI.3.6.Ex, ELD.PI.3.6.Br, ELD.PII.3.2b.Ex, ELD.PII.3.2b.Br
See the California Standards section.

Bats send sound waves out through their mouth or nose. These sound waves hit objects and then bounce back as an **echo**. The echo tells the bats how far away an object is and how big it is. This information helps bats find bugs to eat. It is also an effective way to keep bats from bumping into trees and other bats.

How Bats Use Sound Waves

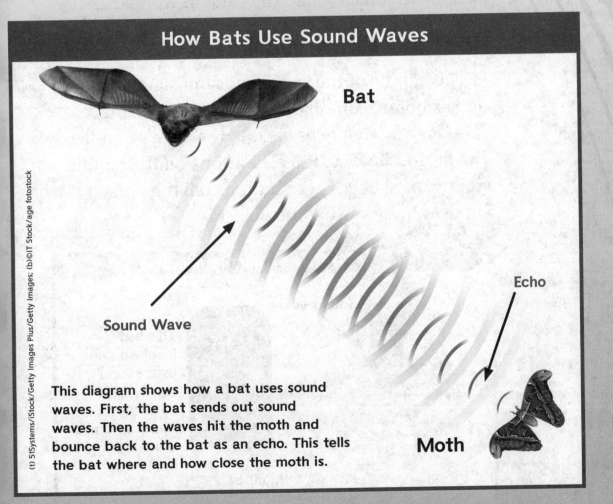

Bat

Echo

Sound Wave

Moth

This diagram shows how a bat uses sound waves. First, the bat sends out sound waves. Then the waves hit the moth and bounce back to the bat as an echo. This tells the bat where and how close the moth is.

ELD.PI.3.1.Ex, ELD.PI.3.1.Br, ELD.PI.3.6.Ex, ELD.PI.3.6.Br See the California Standards section.

Text Evidence

1 **Sentence Structure** (A)(C)(T)

Reread the second sentence. Circle the subject of the sentence. Underline the two actions in the predicate.

2 **Specific Vocabulary** (A)(C)(T)

Read the second sentence. What words in the sentence tell you the meaning of the word *echo*? Draw a box around the words.

COLLABORATE

3 **Talk About It**

How do echoes from sound waves help bats? Write your ideas. Cite text evidence.

_____

_____

_____

1 Sentence Structure A C T

Read sentences six and seven in the first paragraph. Circle the connecting word that shows a sequence of events. Underline what the scientist did after he built the cane.

2 Comprehension

Main Idea and Key Details

Reread the heading for the second paragraph. Then reread the key details in the paragraph. Write the main idea of the paragraph.

_____

_____

3 Specific Vocabulary A C T

Reread the second paragraph. The word *vibrate* means "to shake quickly." What vibrates on the cane? Circle the words that tell you.

A Batty Idea

The scientist who invented the new cane took what he learned from observing bats. He used a similar idea. He started with an **ordinary** white cane. He wanted the cane to imitate the way bats use sound waves. So, he sketched plans and made a model of his invention. When he built the cane, the scientist used a special material that was lightweight and strong. Then he added sound waves. Finally, a team of scientists tested the cane. It worked!

How the Cane Works

The handle of the cane sends out signals. The signals bounce off objects in front of the cane. Then an echo bounces back to the cane's handle. The person holding it feels buttons on the handle **vibrate**, or shake. These buttons tell the person how far away and how big the object is.

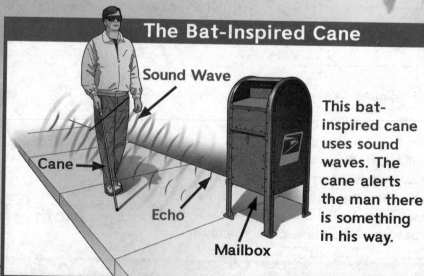

The Bat-Inspired Cane

Sound Wave

Cane

Echo

Mailbox

This bat-inspired cane uses sound waves. The cane alerts the man there is something in his way.

Steve Schell

ELD.PI.3.1.Ex, ELD.PI.3.1.Br, ELD.PI.3.6.Ex, ELD.PI.3.6.Br, ELD.PII.3.2b.Ex, ELD.PII.2b.Br
See the California Standards section.

Scientists and **inventors** study plants and animals all the time. Their **observations** have led them to invent many useful things. And like many new inventions, the bat-inspired cane is a good example of how great ideas can come from nature.

This scientist is studying how bats fly.

Lynn Johnson/Contributor National Geographic/Getty Images

Make Connections

? How did bats inspire a cane that helps blind people? ESSENTIAL QUESTION

What is something in nature that inspires you? What would you invent? TEXT TO SELF

ELD.PI.3.1.Ex, ELD.PI.3.1.Br, ELD.PI.3.6.Ex, ELD.PI.3.6.Br, ELD.PII.3.2a.Ex, ELD.PII.3.2a.Br
See the California Standards section.

Text Evidence

1 **Specific Vocabulary**

Circle the root word in *inventor*. The suffix *-or* means "a person who does something." What does the word *inventor* mean?

_____

2 **Sentence Structure** **ACT**

Look at the last sentence. Circle the comma. The words before the comma give more information about the subject of the sentence. Underline the subject of the sentence.

COLLABORATE

3 **Talk About It**

Why do scientists study plants and animals? Use text evidence.

_____

_____

Respond to the Text

Partner Discussion Work with a partner. Answer the questions. Discuss what you learned about "Bats Did It First." Write the page numbers where you found text evidence.

How do bats navigate at night?

Bats make _____.

The sound waves _____.

The echo tells bats _____.

_____.

Text Evidence

Page(s): _____

Page(s): _____

Page(s): _____

How was the new cane for blind people invented?

A scientist observed bats _____.

He created _____.

The cane uses an echo to _____.

Text Evidence

Page(s): _____

Page(s): _____

Page(s): _____

Group Discussion Present your answers to the group. Cite text evidence to justify your thinking. Listen to and discuss the group's opinions about your answers.

COLLABORATE

Write Work with a partner. Review your notes about "Bats Did It First." Then write your answer to the Essential Question. Use text evidence to support your answer. Use vocabulary words in your writing.

What idea did scientists get from bats?

Bats make sound waves that _____

_____.

A scientist watched _____ and created _____

_____.

The cane uses _____

_____.

The cane helps blind people _____.

COLLABORATE

Share Writing Present your writing to the class. Discuss their opinions. Think about what the class has to say. Did they justify their claims? Explain why you agree or disagree with their claims.

I agree with _____.

That's a good comment, but _____.

Write to Sources

pages 200–205

Take Notes About the Text I took notes on this chart to answer the question: *Why is the new cane better than other canes? Use details from the text.*

Aisha

Main Idea	Details
The new cane is better than other canes. It tells blind people how far away objects are.	The cane sends out signals like a bat.
	Other canes do not send out signals.
	The cane vibrates and tells the person how far away an object is.

Write About the Text I used notes from my chart to write an informative paragraph about the new cane.

Student Model: *Informative Text*

The new cane is better than other canes because it tells blind people how far away objects are. It sends out signals like a bat. Other canes cannot do this.

The cane sends out signals, and the signals hit objects in front of the cane. The person holding the cane will feel the cane vibrate. The cane is a good invention because it helps blind people walk and move around.

TALK ABOUT IT

Text Evidence

Draw a box around the second sentence. Why does Aisha use this information as a supporting detail?

Grammar

Circle the sentence about the person holding the cane. What is the future-tense verb?

Connect Ideas

Underline the second and third sentences. How can you combine these sentences?

Your Turn

How does the author help us understand how bats use signals? Use details from the text.

>> Go Digital
Write your response online. Use your editing checklist.

ELD.PI.3.1.Ex, ELD.PI.3.1.Br, ELD.PI.3.10a.Ex, ELD.PI.3.10a.Br, ELD.PI.3.10b.Ex, ELD.PI.3.10b.Br, ELD.PII.3.1.Ex, ELD.PII.3.1.Br, ELD.PII.3.3.Ex, ELD.PII.3.3.Br, ELD.PII.3.6.Ex, ELD.PII.3.6.Br See the California Standards section.

COLLABORATE

How did Christopher Columbus travel to America? How is this different from the ways people travel today? Write ways that people travel now and long ago in the web.

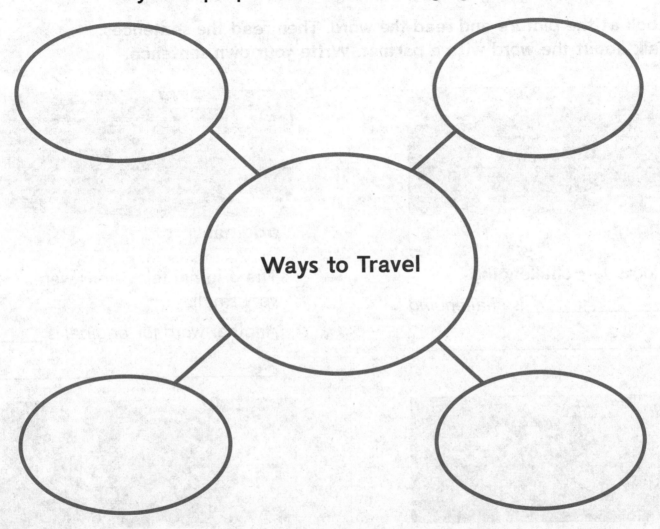

Ways to Travel

Discuss how people traveled in the past. Use the words you wrote. You can say:

People used _____ to travel _____.

People also traveled by _____.

ELD.PI.3.1.Ex, ELD.PI.3.1.Br, ELD.PI.3.12.Ex, ELD.PI.3.12.Br, ELD.PII.3.5.Ex, ELD.PII.3.5.Br See the California Standards section.

More Vocabulary

Look at the picture and read the word. Then read the sentences. Talk about the word with a partner. Write your own sentence.

challenging

This sport looks very **challenging**.

I think _____ is *challenging*

because _____.

original

The **original** televisions were very small.

Another word for *original* is _____

_____.

journey

The people are on a **journey** in the desert.

I want to take a *journey* to _____

_____.

prepared

Dana is **prepared** for the cold.

Another word for *prepared* is _____

_____.

ELD.PI.3.1.Ex, ELD.PI.3.1.Br, ELD.PI.3.5.Ex, ELD.PI.3.5.Br, ELD.PI.3.12.Ex, ELD.PI.3.12.Br See the California Standards section.

successful

The show was **successful**.

I am *successful* when _____

_____ .

uncomfortable

The middle seat is really **uncomfortable**.

I feel *uncomfortable* when _____

_____ .

Words and Phrases
Multiple-Meaning Words

Some words have more than one meaning.

hard = difficult, not easy
The reading test was <u>hard</u>.

hard = uses a lot of energy or effort
Raking leaves is <u>hard</u> work.

Circle the correct meaning of *hard* in each sentence.

The math problem was <u>hard</u> to solve.

not easy   used a lot of energy

Dad worked <u>hard</u> in the yard.

not easy   used a lot of energy

>> *Go Digital* Add the word *hard* to your New Words notebook. Write sentences to show the different meanings.

(t)Adam Taylor/Getty Images; (b)Cohen/Ostrow/Photodisc/Getty Images

COLLABORATE

1 Talk About It

Look at the photograph. Read the title. Discuss what you see. Write your ideas.

What does the title tell you?

_____

_____

_____

_____

What does the photograph show?

_____

_____

_____

_____

Take notes as you read the text.

Essential Question

? How is each event in history unique?

Read to see how the pioneers found their way to Oregon.

Pioneers crossed America in covered wagons like these.

Greg Ryan/Alamy

ELD.PI.3.1.Ex, ELD.PI.3.1.Br, ELD.PI.3.6.Ex, ELD.PI.3.6.Br See the California Standards section.

The Long Road to Oregon

In the spring of 1843, more than 800 pioneers began a **journey** from Independence, Missouri to Oregon City, Oregon. They had 120 wagons and 5,000 cattle. This was one of the first wagon trains to travel west on the Oregon Trail.

Land of Promise

Life was very hard in Missouri in the 1800s. Bad weather caused crops to die. Businesses closed. As a result, many people could not find jobs.

Americans wanted a more enjoyable life. They wanted to live in a place where the soil was **richer** and the weather was more agreeable and pleasant.

The United States government was giving away free land to pioneers. So, thousands of people traveled west to Oregon, a territory in the northwest part of the country.

This map shows the Oregon Trail in 1843.

The Oregon Trail

OREGON CITY

OREGON COUNTRY

UNORGANIZED TERRITORY

IOWA

MEXICAN TERRITORY

Independence

MISSOURI

REPUBLIC OF TEXAS

KEY
~ Trail
• Cities

ELD.PI.3.1.Ex, ELD.PI.3.1.Br, ELD.PI.3.6.Ex, ELD.PI.3.6.Br See the California Standards section.

Text Evidence

1 Sentence Structure Ⓐ Ⓒ Ⓣ

Look at the first sentence in the first paragraph. Which words describe where the journey began? Circle the words. Which words tell where the journey ended? Underline the words.

2 Specific Vocabulary Ⓐ Ⓒ Ⓣ

The word *richer* can mean "has more money" or "filled with things that plants need." What is the meaning of *richer* in this sentence? Circle the meaning above.

COLLABORATE

3 Talk About It

Discuss why Americans wanted to move to Oregon in the 1800s. Cite text evidence.

_____

_____

_____

215

1 Sentence Structure Ⓐ Ⓒ Ⓣ

Reread sentence one in the first paragraph. The sentence has two parts. Underline the part that tells what the pioneers knew. Circle the connecting word.

2 Comprehension

Sequence

Look at the second paragraph. Circle the sequence words that connect the events. Then write the events in order.

_____

_____

_____

3 Specific Vocabulary Ⓐ Ⓒ Ⓣ

A *determined* person plans to do something and cannot be stopped. What were the pioneers determined to do? Underline the words.

Getting Ready to Go

Pioneers knew that emigration from Missouri would be difficult. The trip was more than 2,000 miles of dusty, bumpy trails and would take at least five months. The pioneers needed to be **prepared**.

First they gathered their cows and chickens. Then they packed many pounds of food, cooking pots, tools, and seeds.

Covered wagons were the main form of transportation on the Oregon Trail. The wagons were stuffed with everything a family would need. There was little room for anything else. As a result, children left books, toys, and most of their clothes behind.

A Long, Hard Journey

Planning and packing took weeks. The first thing pioneer families did was hook a team of oxen up to their wagons. Oxen were dependable and strong and could pull the heavy vehicles. Next the families joined other pioneer families.

All the wagons traveling together formed a wagon train. The children and healthy adults walked. The sick or tired pioneers rode in the **uncomfortable** wagons.

Dirty water, sickness, and fierce dust storms made the journey **challenging**. Bad weather often made the trail impassable. But the pioneers were **determined**. As a result, they finally reached their new home in Oregon.

This reenactment shows a wagon train on the Oregon Trail.

Greg Ryan/Alamy

ELD.PI.3.1.Ex, ELD.PI.3.1.Br, ELD.PI.3.6.Ex, ELD.PI.3.6.Br, ELD.PII.3.1.Ex, ELD.PII.3.1.Br, ELD.PII.3.2b.Ex, ELD.PII.3.2b.Br See the California Standards section.

A New Life in Oregon

When the pioneers got to Oregon, they cleared land and built houses. Then they planted crops. As more emigrants arrived, towns grew. People opened stores and restaurants. Businesses boomed. The pioneers worked hard to make their new towns **successful**. They had found a better life!

Many of the people who live in Oregon today are descendants of the brave pioneers who made the journey west from the 1840s to the 1880s. They appreciate their family members' hard work and courage. They are **grateful** for the Oregon Trail.

Learn Your History!

History is the study of people and events from the past. It's important to know our country's past. Learning about history helps us appreciate our country and the people who helped build it.

One fun way to learn about history is by reading the stories of the brave people who lived it. You can read diaries of pioneers on the Oregon Trail, or biographies of explorers. These can be more exciting and inspiring than a movie or a television show!

You can still see parts of the original Oregon Trail today.

Make Connections

 Why was the Oregon Trail emigration a unique time in history? ESSENTIAL QUESTION

What is your favorite event in history? Describe why. TEXT TO SELF

ELD.PI.3.1.Ex, ELD.PI.3.1.Br, ELD.PI.3.3.Ex, ELD.PI.3.3.Br, ELD.PI.3.6.Ex, ELD.PI.3.6.Br, ELD.PI.3.11.Ex, ELD.PI.3.11.Br, ELD.PII.3.1.Ex, ELD.PII.3.1.Br, ELD.PII.3.2b.Ex, ELD.PII.3.2b.Br
See the California Standards section.

Text Evidence

1 Comprehension

Sequence

Look at sentences one and two in the first paragraph. Underline what happened after the pioneers built houses. Circle the connecting word.

2 Specific Vocabulary A C T

Reread the second paragraph. The word *grateful* means "thankful." Circle what the descendants of pioneers are grateful for.

COLLABORATE

3 Talk About It

What words in paragraph one of "Learn Your History!" show the author's opinion? Discuss what words the author uses to support the opinion. Do you agree or disagree with the opinion? Give evidence to support your opinion.

Respond to the Text

Partner Discussion Work with a partner. Answer the questions. Discuss what you learned about "The Long Road to Oregon." Write the page numbers where you found text evidence.

How did the pioneers get ready to travel to Oregon?

Pioneers gathered _____.   Text Evidence Page(s): _____

In the wagons, they packed _____

_____.   Page(s): _____

Then they joined other _____.   Page(s): _____

What was the journey on the Oregon Trail like?

Oxen pulled _____.   Text Evidence Page(s): _____

Children and healthy adults _____.   Page(s): _____

The journey to Oregon was _____.   Page(s): _____

Group Discussion Present your answers to the group. Cite text evidence to justify your thinking. Listen to and discuss the group's opinions about your answers.

Write Work with a partner. Review your notes about "The Long Road to Oregon." Then write your answer to the Essential Question. Use text evidence to support your answer. Use vocabulary words from this week's reading in your writing.

Why was the journey on the Oregon Trail unique?

The pioneers left home to _____

_____.

They traveled with _____

_____.

The journey to Oregon was _____

_____.

Share Writing Present your writing to the class. Discuss their opinions. Think about what the class has to say. Did they justify their claims? Explain why you agree or disagree with their claims.

I agree with _____.

That's a good comment, but _____.

Write to Sources

pages 214–217

Micco

Take Notes About the Text I took notes on this idea web to answer the question: *In your opinion, does the author do a good job of describing the pioneers' journey on the Oregon Trail?*

The author says the journey was more than 2,000 miles.

The author says the journey took five months.

The author does a good job of describing the journey.

The author says trails were dusty and bumpy.

The author says there was dirty water, sickness, and dust storms.

Write About the Text I used notes from my idea web to write an opinion about how well the author describes the pioneers' journey.

Student Model: *Opinion*

I think the author does a good job of describing the pioneers' journey on the Oregon Trail. The author uses many details to describe the journey. The trip was more than 2,000 miles. It took five months. The trails were dusty. The trails were bumpy. The author says that there was dirty water, sickness, and dust storms. These details help me picture the difficult journey.

TALK ABOUT IT
COLLABORATE

Text Evidence

Circle a sentence that comes from the notes. Why does Micco include this detail?

Grammar

Circle the pronoun in the fourth sentence. What does the pronoun refer to?

Condense Ideas

Underline the sentences about the trails. How can you condense the sentences?

Your Turn
COLLABORATE

In your opinion, was it a good idea for people to move to Oregon in the 1800s? Use details from the text.

≫ Go Digital
Write your response online. Use your editing checklist.

ELD.PI.3.1.Ex, ELD.PI.3.1.Br, ELD.PI.3.3.Ex, ELD.PI.3.3.Br, ELD.PI.3.10a.Ex, ELD.PI.3.10a.Br, ELD.PI.3.10b.Ex, ELD.PI.3.10b.Br, ELD.PI.3.11.Ex, ELD.PI.3.11.Br, ELD.PII.3.2a.Ex, ELD.PII.3.2a.Br, ELD.PII.3.7.Ex, ELD.PII.3.7.Br See the California Standards section.

Unit 4

Meet the Challenge

The Big Idea

What are different ways to meet challenges?

TALK ABOUT IT

Weekly Concept Choices

? **Essential Question**

What choices are good for us?

» *Go Digital*

224

What is the girl in the picture doing? What healthy choice did the girl make? Write healthy choices in the chart. Describe why the choices are healthy.

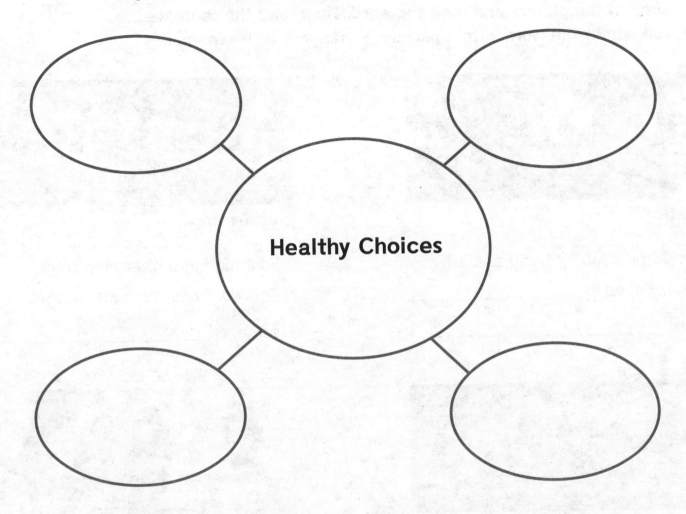

Healthy Choices

Discuss why some choices are healthy. Use the words from the chart. You can say:

Choose to _____ to feed your body _____.

Choose to _____ to stay in good _____.

Choose to _____ to do well in _____.

ELD.PI.3.1.Ex, ELD.PI.3.1.Br, ELD.PI.3.2.Ex, ELD.PI.3.2.Br, ELD.PII.3.3.Ex, ELD.PII.3.3.Br See the California Standards section.

McGraw-Hill Companies, Inc. Tonika G. Johnson, Photographer

More Vocabulary

COLLABORATE

Look at the picture and read the word. Then read the sentences. Talk about the word with a partner. Write your own sentence.

admiration

Tina has **admiration** for her grandfather.

I have *admiration* for _____

because _____.

approached

The bear **approached** the water to drink.

This morning, I *approached* _____

_____.

charming

Eduardo has a **charming** smile.

The word *charming* means the

same as _____.

contributions

We made **contributions** to the food drive.

People make *contributions* because _____

_____.

(ul)Ron Levine/Getty Images; (ur)Image Source/Alamy; (bl)TNWA Photography/Moment Open/Getty Images; (br)Ken Karp/McGraw-Hill Education

pretended

Tim **pretended** to fly.

Sometimes I *pretend* _____

_____ .

wealth

Carla counted her **wealth**.

Another word for *wealth* is

_____

_____ .

Words and Phrases
Suffixes: *-ful* and *-y*

The suffixes *-ful* and *-y* both mean "full of." Add *-ful* or *-y* to a noun and make an adjective.

healthy = full of health.
Healthy *food is good for you.*

flavorful = full of flavor.
The soup is flavorful.

Read the sentences below. Write the word that means the same as the underlined word or words.

The sky is full of clouds.

The sky is _____ .

              cloudier   cloudy

The apple is full of color.

The apple is _____ .

            coloring   colorful

» Go Digital **Add these words with suffixes to your New Words notebook. Write a sentence to show the meaning of each.**

1 Talk About It

Look at the illustration. Read the title. Discuss what you see. Write your ideas.

What does the title tell you about the story?

_____

_____

_____

_____

What does the illustration show?

_____

_____

_____

_____

Take notes as you read the story.

Nail Soup

Essential Question

? **What choices are good for us?**

Read about how choices helped a man and his wife learn a lesson.

ELD.PI.3.1.Ex, ELD.PI.3.1.Br, ELD.PI.3.6.Ex, ELD.PI.3.6.Br See the California Standards section.

Once long ago, Papa and I were walking for miles on a long and winding country road. Finally we **approached** a large farmhouse surrounded by fields of healthy vegetables.

"Papa, I'm so hungry," I said.

Papa patted my head and winked. I smiled and nodded back. I admired my Papa. I knew he would find a way to get us a warm meal. We knocked on the door, and a well-dressed man and his wife answered.

"Hello," said Papa. "My son, Erik, is hungry. Could you please spare a **morsel** of food?"

The man shook his head. "We have lots of food, but we cannot afford to give any of it away," he said.

"Well, I could cook my flavorful nail soup if you would donate a small cup of hot water," said Papa.

The woman looked at her husband. "Soup from a nail?" she said. "That's impossible." But the man's curiosity overwhelmed him, so he brought a small cup of boiling water.

ELD.PI.3.6.Ex, ELD.PI.3.6.Br See the California Standards section.

1 Comprehension

Point of View

Reread the third paragraph. How does the boy feel about his father? Underline the text evidence that tells you.

2 Sentence Structure Ⓐ Ⓒ Ⓣ

Reread the last sentence in the third paragraph. Underline the word that connects the two clauses. Which clause tells what happened after Erik and Papa knocked on the door? Underline the clause.

3 Specific Vocabulary Ⓐ Ⓒ Ⓣ

Look at the fourth paragraph. The word *morsel* means "a small amount." What kind of morsel does Papa ask for? Write the word.

Text Evidence

1 Sentence Structure ACT

Reread the first paragraph. An adjective is a word that describes a noun. Circle the five adjectives in this paragraph.

Which adjectives describe the nail? Write the words.

_____

_____

2 Comprehension
Point of View

Reread the third paragraph. Why does the boy's admiration for his Papa grow? Underline text evidence that tells you.

3 Specific Vocabulary ACT

Look at the word *impolite*. The word *impolite* means "not polite" or "rude." Underline the words that show what action is impolite.

Papa carefully took out a long, crooked nail and with one graceful motion, dropped it into the cup. He stirred the cup of hot liquid.

"This is beginning to smell wonderful," said Papa.

I smiled at Papa. He was clever and **charming**, and my **admiration** for him grew. He could do anything! Then I remembered something he taught me.

"Papa, it is **impolite** for me to eat nail soup without offering some to everyone," I said. "But there is such a small amount here."

"We can't let the boy eat alone," said the man to his wife. "We can spare more water."

The woman filled a big pot with water and put it on the stove. When the water boiled, Papa placed the nail into the pot, stirred, and sniffed the air. "The aroma is good, but it would be much more aromatic with an onion. Have you any old onions?"

The woman gave Papa three small onions, and he dropped them into the pot.

"Papa, remember how luscious nail soup was with carrots?" I asked.

ELD.PI.3.1.Ex, ELD.PI.3.1.Br, ELD.PI.3.6.Ex, ELD.PI.3.6.Br, ELD.PI.3.7.Ex, ELD.PI.3.7.Br
See the California Standards section.

The man jumped up and pulled four plump carrots from a large basket of vegetables on the floor. "How about some beets and cabbages, too?" he said. "I can spare a few of those."

"And here are some potatoes and green beans," the woman interrupted. "They are healthful and **nutritious contributions**. We grow them ourselves!"

Papa dropped the vegetables into the boiling water while the man grabbed a variety of spices and meats. "Here, add these, too," he said enthusiastically.

Soon the soup was ready, and we sat down to eat. I knew the man and his wife would enjoy nail soup.

"This soup is amazing," said the woman. "And all from just one nail and a pot of boiling water."

Papa **pretended** to be surprised by her amazement, but as usual, he had the perfect answer. "What did you expect?" he said. "I told you it would be flavorful."

The man and woman smiled. "We just didn't know that sharing a little of our great **wealth** would taste so good!"

Illustrator: B Gerardo Suzan

Make Connections

? Why is making nail soup a smart choice? ESSENTIAL QUESTION

How do you feel when you make good choices? TEXT TO SELF

Text Evidence

1 Specific Vocabulary Ⓐ Ⓒ Ⓣ

Look at the word *nutritious*. When a food is nutritious, it has the things your body needs to grow and be healthy. Circle the word in the paragraph that has the same meaning as *nutritious*.

2 Sentence Structure Ⓐ Ⓒ Ⓣ

Reread the first sentence in the third paragraph. The word *while* connects two actions that happen at the same time. Underline Papa's action. Circle the man's action.

COLLABORATE

3 Talk About It

How do the man and woman feel about sharing by the end of the story? Cite text evidence.

_____

_____

_____

Respond to the Text

Partner Discussion Work with a partner. Answer the questions. Discuss what you learned about "Nail Soup." Write the page numbers where you found text evidence.

How do the characters in the story make nail soup?

First, Papa _____.

Then he _____.

The man and the woman _____.

Text Evidence 🔍

Page(s): _____

Page(s): _____

Page(s): _____

How do the man and woman feel about sharing?

At first, the man says _____.

While Papa makes nail soup, _____.

In the end, the man and woman say _____.

Text Evidence 🔍

Page(s): _____

Page(s): _____

Page(s): _____

Group Discussion Present your answers to the group. Cite text evidence to justify your thinking. Listen to and discuss the group's opinions about your answers.

COLLABORATE

Write Review your notes about "Nail Soup." Then write your answer to the Essential Question. Use text evidence to support your answer. Use vocabulary words from this week's reading in your writing.

How do the man and woman's choices help them learn a lesson?

When Papa asks for some food, _____

_____.

Then Papa says he will _____.

The man and woman choose to _____.

They contribute _____.

In the end, the man and woman feel _____

_____.

The man and woman learn that _____.

COLLABORATE

Share Writing Present your writing to the class. Discuss their opinions. Think about what the class has to say. Did they justify their claims? Explain why you agree or disagree with their claims. You can say:

I think your idea is _____.

That's a good comment, but _____.

Write to Sources

Lizzie

Take Notes About the Text I took notes on this chart to answer the question: *Do you think Papa's plan to make nail soup is a good idea? Use details from the story to support your answer.*

The man and woman will not give Papa any food.

↓

Papa asks for a cup of hot water to make nail soup.

↓

Papa tricks the man and woman so they give him vegetables for the soup.

↓

The man and woman put vegetables in the soup.

altrendo images/Stockbyte/Getty Images

234 ELD.PI.3.6.Ex, ELD.PI.3.6.Br See the California Standards section.

Write About the Text I used notes to write an opinion.
I supported my opinion with details from the text.

Student Model: *Opinion*

Papa's plan to make nail soup is a good idea. The unfriendly man and woman will not give Papa any food. So Papa asks for a cup of hot water. He puts a nail in the water. He says he will make nail soup. Then Papa tricks the man and woman. He gets them to put vegetables in the soup. Then everyone eats the soup together. Papa's idea is good. He gets food for himself and his son.

TALK ABOUT IT

Text Evidence

Underline the second sentence. What word does Lizzie use to add more information about the man and woman?

Grammar

Draw a box around the sentence about Papa's plan. What is the linking verb in the sentence?

Connect Ideas

Circle the last two sentences. How can you combine the sentences to connect the ideas?

Your Turn

In your opinion, do the man and his wife make good choices? Use text evidence to support your answer.

>> Go Digital
Write your response online. Use your editing checklist.

ELD.PI.3.1.Ex, ELD.PI.3.1.Br, ELD.PI.3.3.Ex, ELD.PI.3.3.Br, ELD.PI.3.10a.Ex, ELD.PI.3.10a.Br, ELD.PI.3.10b.Ex, ELD.PI.3.10b.Br, ELD.PI.3.11.Ex,
ELD.PI.3.11.Br, ELD.PII.3.3.Ex, ELD.PII.3.3.Br, ELD.PII.3.4.Ex, ELD.PII.3.4.Br, ELD.PII.3.6.Ex, ELD.PII.3.6.Br See the California Standards section. **235**

TALK ABOUT IT

Weekly Concept Skills and Talents

? **Essential Question**
How can you use what you know to help others?

>> *Go Digital*

COLLABORATE

Look at the picture. How is the man using his talents to help others? Write other talents in the chart. Discuss how you can use the talents.

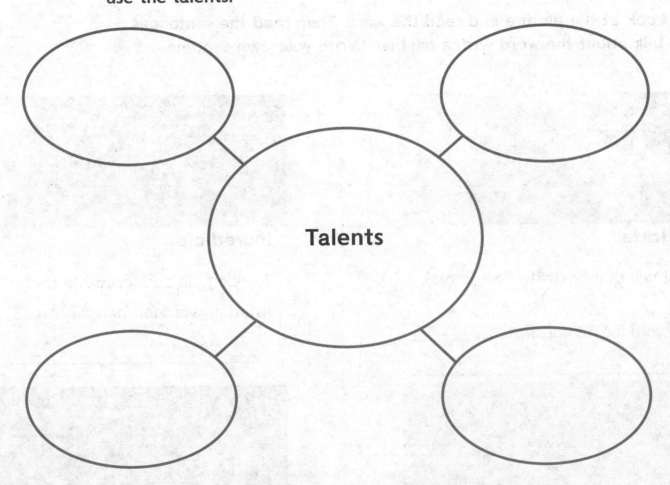

Talents

Discuss how you can use your talents to help others. Use the words from the chart. You can say:

You can use _____ to _____.

You can use _____ to _____.

You can use _____ to _____.

You can use _____ to _____.

ELD.PI.3.1.Ex, ELD.PI.3.1.Br, ELD.PI.3.2.Ex, ELD.PI.3.2.Br, ELD.PII.3.3.Ex, ELD.PII.3.3.Br See the California Standards section.

More Vocabulary

COLLABORATE

Look at the picture and read the word. Then read the sentences.
Talk about the word with a partner. Write your own sentence.

demonstrate

The artist will **demonstrate** how to make a pot.

Another word for *demonstrate* is _____

_____ .

impossible

It is **impossible** to walk across the bridge.

It is *impossible* to _____

_____ .

incredible

The dog did an **incredible** trick.

Another word for *incredible* is _____

_____

location

The park is a good **location** for a walk.

What is a good *location* for a soccer game?

_____

_____ .

ELD.PI.3.1.Ex, ELD.PI.3.1.Br, ELD.PI.3.5.Ex, ELD.PI.3.5.Br, ELD.PI.3.12.Ex, ELD.PI.3.12.Br See the California Standards section.

relaxed

Anna feels calm and **relaxed**.

I feel *relaxed* when _____

_____.

remember

A list helps Mom **remember** what to buy.

I need to *remember* _____

_____.

Words and Phrases
Sentences with *that*

The word *that* is used in different ways.

That **is a conjunction.** ***That*** **connects two ideas.**
I think <u>*that*</u> *dogs are great animals.*

That **can also be a pronoun. It tells which one.**
<u>*That*</u> *is a good idea.*

Read each sentence. Write the word *that*
to complete it.

I know _____ it is raining.

_____ is a big tree.

Write your own sentences using *that*. **Use it as a**
conjunction and as a pronoun.

_____

_____

>> *Go Digital* **Add the word** *that* **to your New**
Words notebook. Include your sentences.

COLLABORATE

1 Talk About It

Look at the illustration. Read the title. Discuss what you see. Write your ideas.

What does the title tell you?

_____

_____

_____

Who is in the illustration?

_____

_____

_____

Where does the story take place?

_____

_____

_____

Take notes as you read the story.

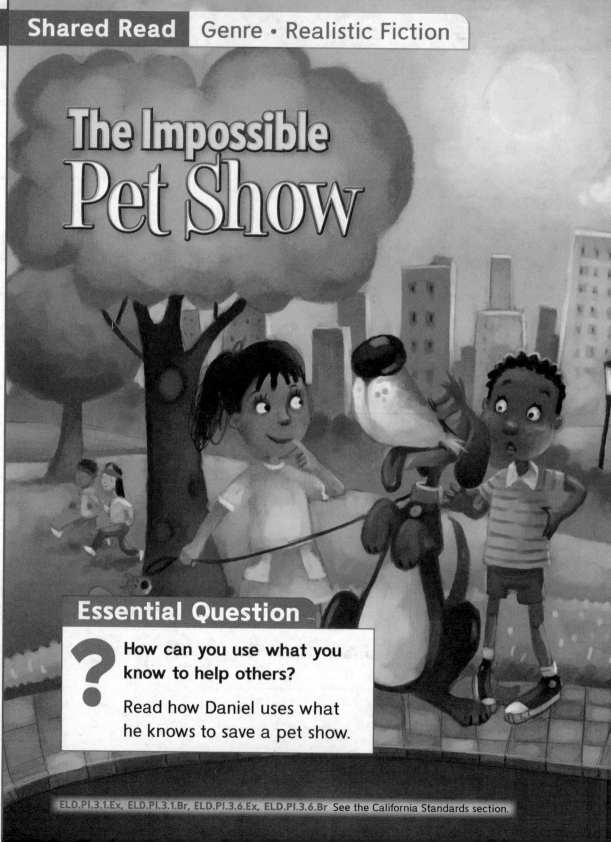

The Impossible Pet Show

Essential Question

? **How can you use what you know to help others?**

Read how Daniel uses what he knows to save a pet show.

ELD.PI.3.1.Ex, ELD.PI.3.1.Br, ELD.PI.3.6.Ex, ELD.PI.3.6.Br See the California Standards section.

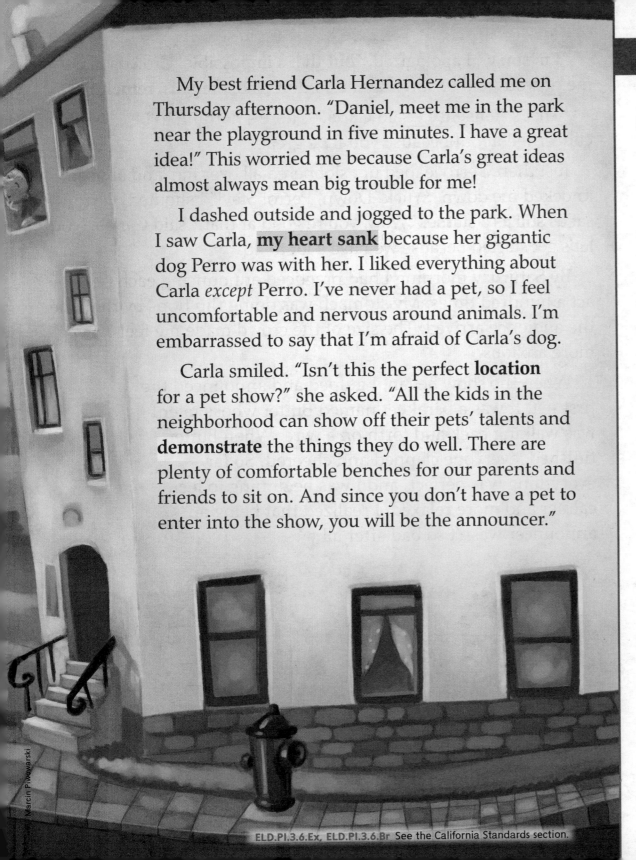

My best friend Carla Hernandez called me on Thursday afternoon. "Daniel, meet me in the park near the playground in five minutes. I have a great idea!" This worried me because Carla's great ideas almost always mean big trouble for me!

I dashed outside and jogged to the park. When I saw Carla, **my heart sank** because her gigantic dog Perro was with her. I liked everything about Carla *except* Perro. I've never had a pet, so I feel uncomfortable and nervous around animals. I'm embarrassed to say that I'm afraid of Carla's dog.

Carla smiled. "Isn't this the perfect **location** for a pet show?" she asked. "All the kids in the neighborhood can show off their pets' talents and **demonstrate** the things they do well. There are plenty of comfortable benches for our parents and friends to sit on. And since you don't have a pet to enter into the show, you will be the announcer."

Text Evidence

1 Comprehension

Point of View

Reread the first paragraph. How does Daniel feel about Carla's idea? Circle the word that shows how Daniel feels.

2 Specific Vocabulary Ⓐ Ⓒ Ⓣ

Look at the second paragraph. The phrase *my heart sank* means "I had a bad feeling." Why does Daniel say "my heart sank?"

_____

_____

3 Sentence Structure Ⓐ Ⓒ Ⓣ

Reread sentence three in the last paragraph. Which noun does the pronoun *they* refer to? Write the noun.

_____

ELD.PI.3.6.Ex, ELD.PI.3.6.Br See the California Standards section.

241

1 Sentence Structure Ⓐ🅒Ⓣ

Reread the first paragraph. Circle the punctuation marks that show someone is speaking. Underline the pronoun that shows who is speaking. Then write the name of the speaker.

_____

2 Specific Vocabulary Ⓐ🅒Ⓣ

Look at the word *nonsense*. The prefix *non-* means "no" or "not." Circle the prefix. Underline the root word *sense*. What does the word *nonsense* mean?

_____

3 Comprehension

Point of View

Reread the last paragraph. How does Daniel feel after everyone claps and cheers?

_____

"I'm sorry," I apologized, "but that's **impossible**! Crowds make me nervous and unsure. Besides, I don't like animals, **remember**?"

"That's **nonsense**," said Carla. "There's nothing to be concerned about because you'll be great!"

Just then, Perro leaped up, slobbered all over me, and almost knocked me down. "Yuck. Down, Perro! Stay!" I shouted. Perro sat as still as a statue. "Wow, you're good at that," said Carla. "Now let's get started because we have a lot to do."

By Saturday morning I had practiced announcing each pet's act a hundred times. My stomach was doing flip flops by the time the audience arrived. The size of the crowd made me feel even more anxious.

When the show began, I gulped and announced the first pet. It was a parakeet named Butter whose talent was walking back and forth on a wire. When Butter finished, everyone clapped and cheered. So far, everything was perfect, and I was beginning to feel calmer and more **relaxed**. I realized that being an announcer wasn't so bad after all.

ELD.PI.3.6.Ex, ELD.PI.3.6.Br See the California Standards section.

Then it was Carla and Perro's turn.

"Sit, Perro," she said, but Perro didn't sit.

Perro was not paying attention to Carla. He was too interested in watching Jack's bunnies jump in and out of their boxes. Suddenly, Perro leaped at the bunnies who hopped toward Mandy and knocked over her hamster's cage. Pudgy, the hamster, escaped and began running around in circles while Kyle's dog, Jake, howled. This was a **disaster**, and I had to do something.

"Sit!" I shouted at Perro. "Quiet!" I ordered Jake. "Stay!" I yelled. Everyone – kids and pets – stopped and stared at me. Even the audience froze.

"Daniel, that was **incredible**," said Carla. "You got the pets to settle down. That's quite an achievement."

Sadly, that was the end of our pet show. But now I have more confidence when I have to speak in front of people. And even though I am still nervous around animals, Perro and I have become great friends. And I've discovered my talent, too.

PET SHOW TODAY

Marcin Piwowarski

Make Connections

? How did Daniel use what he knows to help others? ESSENTIAL QUESTION

Discuss whether you would like to take part in a pet show, and why. TEXT TO SELF

ELD.PI.3.1.Ex, ELD.PI.3.1.Br, ELD.PI.3.6.Ex, ELD.PI.3.6.Br, ELD.PI.3.7.Ex
See the California Standards section.

Text Evidence

1 Sentence Structure Ⓐ Ⓒ Ⓣ

Reread sentence three in the third paragraph. Circle the connecting word *who*. It connects the main clause and a subordinate clause. What do the bunnies do? Underline the the bunnies' actions.

2 Specific Vocabulary Ⓐ Ⓒ Ⓣ

Reread the last sentence in the third paragraph. A *disaster* is a terrible event. Circle one reason that the pet show is a disaster.

COLLABORATE

3 Talk About It

How does Daniel change at the end of the story? Write the text evidence that shows how.

_____

_____

_____

_____

Respond to the Text

COLLABORATE

Partner Discussion Work with a partner. Answer the questions. Discuss what you learned about "The Impossible Pet Show." Write the page numbers where you found text evidence.

What happens at the pet show?

First, Perro _____.

Text Evidence 🔍

Page(s): _____

Next, the bunnies knock over _____.

Page(s): _____

Then the hamster _____.

Page(s): _____

What does Daniel do at the pet show?

First, Daniel shouts at _____.

Text Evidence 🔍

Page(s): _____

Next Daniel orders _____.

Page(s): _____

Finally, Daniel _____ and _____.

Page(s): _____

COLLABORATE

Group Discussion Present your answers to the group. Cite text evidence to justify your thinking. Listen to and discuss the group's opinions about your answers.

Write Review your notes about "The Impossible Pet Show." Then write your answer to the Essential Question. Use text evidence to support your answer. Use vocabulary words from this week's reading in your writing.

> **How does Daniel use what he knows to save the pet show?**
>
> First, Perro _____.
>
> Then, the bunnies_____.
>
> Next, the hamster _____.
>
> Then, Daniel shouts_____.
>
> Next, he orders_____
>
> and everyone_____.
>
> Daniel saves the show because_____
>
> _____.

Share Writing Present your writing to the class. Discuss their opinions. Think about what the class has to say. Did they justify their claims? Explain why you agree or disagree with their claims. Support your opinions with text evidence. You can say

I agree with _____.

That's a good comment, but _____.

ELD.PI.3.1.Ex, ELD.PI.3.1.Br, ELD.PI.3.3.Ex, ELD.PI.3.3.Br, ELD.PI.3.5.Ex, ELD.PI.3.5.Br, ELD.PI.3.6.Ex, ELD.PI.3.6.Br, ELD.PI.3.9.Ex, ELD.PI.3.9.Br, ELD.PI.3.12.Ex, ELD.PI.3.12.Br See the California Standards section.

Write to Sources

pages 240–243

Take Notes About the Text I took notes on this chart to answer the question: *In your opinion, is Daniel a good announcer for the pet show?*

Jamie

Daniel feels nervous.

He does a good job announcing the pets.

The animals start running around and howling.

Daniel tells them to sit and be quiet.

Everyone settles down.

Write About the Text I used notes to write an opinion about Daniel. I used the story to support my opinion.

Student Model: *Opinion*

I think Daniel is a good announcer for the pet show. Daniel is very nervous. But he does a good job announcing the pets. When there is a problem, Daniel solves it. The animals start running around and howling. Daniel tells them to sit and be quiet. Everyone settles down. That is why Daniel is a good announcer for the pet show.

TALK ABOUT IT

COLLABORATE

Text Evidence
Circle the sentence about the animals. Why does Jamie use this sentence to support her opinion?

Grammar
Draw a box around the sentence that tells what Daniel tells the animals. What words can you add to tell when he does this?

Connect Ideas
Underline the sixth and seventh sentences. How can you combine the sentences?

Your Turn

COLLABORATE

In your opinion, would you be a good announcer for the pet show? Tell why or why not.

≫ Go Digital
Write your response online. Use your editing checklist.

TALK ABOUT IT

? **Essential Question**
How do animals adapt to
challenges in their habitat?

» *Go Digital*

248

How does the ermine change to match its habitat? In the chart, write other ways that animals adapt to their habitats. Discuss how different habitats affect animals.

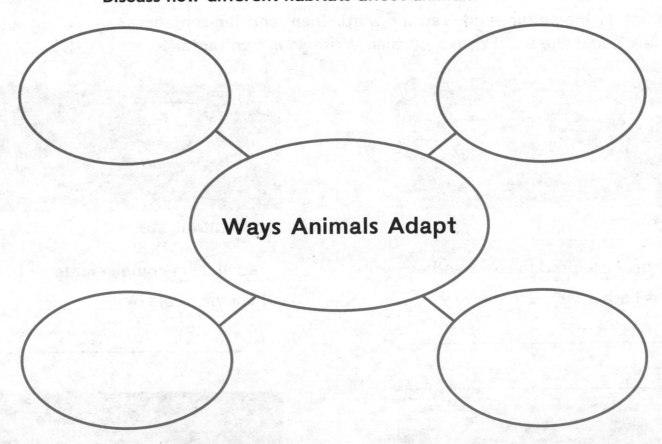

Ways Animals Adapt

Discuss how these adaptations help animals to survive. Use the words from the chart. You can say:

Animals can change their _____ to _____.

Animals have different types of _____ to _____.

Animals grow or lose their _____ depending on

_____.

Animals move at different _____ to _____.

ELD.PI.3.1.Ex, ELD.PI.3.1.Br, ELD.PI.3.2.Ex, ELD.PI.3.2.Br See the California Standards section.

Look at the picture and read the word. Then read the sentences. Talk about the word with a partner. Write your own sentence.

adapted

The polar bear **adapted** to cold weather.

Polar bears have *adapted* to snow by

_____

_____.

communicate

Ted and Em **communicate** by talking.

I *communicate* by _____

_____.

caution

The crossing guard **cautions** cars to stop.

Another word for *caution* is _____

_____.

danger

Fire is a **danger** to forests.

_____ is a *danger* because

_____.

members

The kids are **members** of the band.

I want to be a *member* of _____

_____.

warn

Road signs **warn** drivers to slow down.

Another word for *warn* is _____

_____.

The *–er* ending is used to compare two or more people or things.
*Rosa is **faster** than Mark.*

The *–est* ending is used to compare three or more people or things.
*Jorge is the **fastest** runner in the class.*

Write the word that completes each sentence.

My dog is _____ than my cat.

bigger   biggest

My sister is the _____ person in my family.

smaller   smallest

Write your own sentences using a word that ends in *–er* and a word that ends in *–est*.

_____

_____

» *Go Digital* **Add these words to your New Words notebook. Include your sentences.**

COLLABORATE

1 Talk About It

Look at the photograph. Read the title. Discuss what you see. Write your ideas.

What does the title tell you?

_____

_____

_____

_____

What does the photograph show?

_____

_____

_____

_____

Take notes as you read the text.

GRAY WOLF! RED FOX!

Essential Question

? How do animals adapt to challenges in their habitat?

Read how gray wolves and red foxes adapt to challenges.

ELD.PI.3.1.Ex, ELD.PI.3.1.Br, ELD.PI.3.6.Ex, ELD.PI.3.6.Br See the California Standards section.

Did you ever see a photograph of a gray wolf or a red fox? Don't they look a lot like dogs? Aren't they fantastic-looking animals? Well, dogs, foxes, and wolves are all related. They are all **members** of the same family. And while gray wolves and red foxes may look alike, they are different in many ways.

LOOKS ARE EVERYTHING

The gray wolf is the **largest** member, or a part, of the wild dog family. An adult wolf is the size of a large dog. The red fox is smaller and weighs less. Both animals have excellent hearing. The red fox can even hear small animals digging holes underground.

And just take a look at those beautiful tails! The gray wolf and red fox both have long, bushy tails. The wolf's tail can be two feet long. The fox's tail is not as long but has a bright, white tip. In the winter, foxes use their thick, furry tails as protection from the cold.

The gray wolf and red fox are both mammals.

ELD.PI.3.1.Ex, ELD.PI.3.1.Br, ELD.PI.3.7.Ex, ELD.PI.3.7.Br See the California Standards section.

Text Evidence

1 Specific Vocabulary Ⓐ Ⓒ Ⓣ

Look at the adjective *largest* in the second paragraph. The suffix *-est* at the end of the word means "most." What does *largest* mean?

Circle the noun that *largest* describes.

2 Sentence Structure Ⓐ Ⓒ Ⓣ

Look at the last sentence in the second paragraph. Underline the words that tell what small animals do.

3 Comprehension

Compare and Contrast

Reread the last paragraph. Draw a box around one detail that shows how gray wolves and red foxes are alike.

Text Evidence 🔍

① Specific Vocabulary ⒶⒸⓉ

Look at the word *lost*. In this sentence, it means "does not have something any longer." Circle the sentence that tells habitats that foxes and wolves lost. Draw a box around the sentence that tells why they lost these habitats.

② Sentence Structure ⒶⒸⓉ

Look at the last sentence in the second paragraph. Circle the connecting word *however*. It shows that wolves act in a different way than foxes. Underline the words that tell how wolves are different.

③ Comprehension

Compare and Contrast

Reread the last paragraph. How are the diets of foxes and wolves different?

_____

_____

Foxes and wolves also have thick fur. Their coats can be white, brown, or black. However, red foxes most often have red fur, while a gray wolf's fur is usually more gray and brown.

FINDING FOOD

Gray wolves and red foxes live in many different habitats. They live in forests, deserts, woodlands, and grasslands. But as more people build roads and shopping centers, both animals have **lost** their homes. The red fox has **adapted** well, or made changes, to fit into its environment. Now more foxes make their homes close to towns and parks. Wolves, however, stay far away from towns and people.

Foxes and wolves are not in competition for food. They have different diets. Red foxes prefer to hunt alone and eat small animals, birds, and fish. They also like to raid garbage cans and campsites for food. Wolves work together in packs, or groups, to hunt large animals, such as moose and deer.

Gray wolves prefer to live and hunt in packs.

WHERE DO THEY LIVE?

United States of America

N W E S

LEGEND
- ■ Red Fox only
- ■ Gray Wolf only
- ■ Both

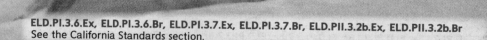

ELD.PI.3.6.Ex, ELD.PI.3.6.Br, ELD.PI.3.7.Ex, ELD.PI.3.7.Br, ELD.PII.3.2b.Ex, ELD.PII.3.2b.Br
See the California Standards section.

DAY-TO-DAY

Wolves live in packs of four to seven. They do almost everything together. They hunt, travel, and choose safe places to set up dens for shelter. Foxes, on the other hand, like to live alone. They usually sleep in the open or find an empty hole to call home.

The red fox hunts for food alone.

Both wolves and foxes **communicate** by barking and growling. The gray wolf also howls to alert, or **warn**, other wolves when there is **danger** nearby. The red fox signals in a different way. It waves its tail in the air to **caution** other foxes.

The gray wolf and red fox are members of the same family and have many things **in common**. But they really are two very different animals.

(tl) Mapping Specialists, Ltd., Madison, WI; (b) Corbis Bridge/Alamy; (tr) jimkruger/iStock/360/Getty Images; (twigs) McGraw-Hill Education

Make Connections

? How have the gray wolf and the red fox adapted to living in North America?
ESSENTIAL QUESTION

Which animal would you like to learn more about? Why?
TEXT TO SELF

Text Evidence

❶ Comprehension
Compare and Contrast

Look at sentence four in the first paragraph. Circle the signal words that show foxes are different from wolves. How are foxes different?

_____

❷ Specific Vocabulary Ⓐ Ⓒ Ⓣ

Reread the first sentence in the last paragraph. The words *in common* mean "sharing the same things." Underline one thing that the fox and wolf have in common.

COLLABORATE

❸ Talk About It

How do gray wolves and red foxes communicate differently? Write your ideas.

_____

_____

ELD.PI.3.1.Ex, ELD.PI.3.1.Br, ELD.PI.3.6.Ex, ELD.PI.3.6.Br See the California Standards section.

Respond to the Text

Partner Discussion Work with a partner. Answer the questions. Discuss what you learned about "Gray Wolf! Red Fox!" Write the page numbers where you found text evidence.

How have red foxes adapted to challenges?

Red foxes use their bushy tails _____.

Text Evidence 🔍

Page(s): _____

In the text, red foxes live near _____.

Page(s): _____

A red fox can hear _____.

Page(s): _____

How have gray wolves adapted to challenges?

Gray wolves hunt in packs because _____.

Text Evidence 🔍

Page(s): _____

According to the author, gray wolves howl to _____.

Page(s): _____

I read that gray wolves have excellent _____.

Page(s): _____

Group Discussion Present your answers to the group. Cite text evidence to justify your thinking. Listen to and discuss the group's opinions about your answers.

Write Work with a partner. Review your notes about "Gray Wolf! Red Fox!" Then write your answer to the Essential Question. Use text evidence to support your answer. Use vocabulary words from this week's reading in your writing.

> **How do gray wolves and red foxes adapt to challenges in their habitats?**
>
> Red foxes live near humans, so they _____.
>
> Gray wolves hunt in packs to _____
>
> _____.
>
> Red foxes use their tails to _____.
>
> On the other hand, gray wolves howl to _____.
>
> Both gray wolves and red foxes _____.

Share Writing Present your writing to the class. Discuss their opinions. Think about what the class has to say. Did they justify their claims? Explain why you agree or disagree with their claims.

I think your idea is _____.

I do not agree because _____.

Write to Sources

pages 252–255

Luke

Take Notes About the Text I took notes about the text on this idea web to answer the question: *How have red foxes adapted to changes in their habitat? Use details from the text in your answer.*

Red foxes moved to live close to towns and parks.

How red foxes adapted

Red foxes look for food in garbage cans.

Red foxes look for food in campsites.

Write About the Text I used my notes to write about how red foxes adapted to changes in their habitat.

Student Model: *Informative Text*

Can red foxes adapt to changes in their habitat? Yes, they can. People built roads and shopping centers. Red foxes lost their homes. But red foxes have adapted. Now they live close to towns and parks. Red foxes look for food in garbage cans. They also eat food in campsites. When their habitat changed, red foxes adapted.

TALK ABOUT IT

COLLABORATE

Text Evidence
Underline the sentence that states the main idea of the paragraph. What evidence does Luke use to support this statement?

Grammar
Box the sentence about towns and parks. **Circle** the pronoun in the sentence. What does the pronoun *they* refer to?

Connect Ideas
Circle the third and fourth sentences. How can you use the word *so* to connect the ideas?

Your Turn

COLLABORATE

How do red foxes and gray wolves live differently? Use details from the text in your response.

>> Go Digital
Write your response online. Use your editing checklist.

COLLABORATE Look at the picture. How is the person flying? Write words about flight in the chart. Talk about how people fly.

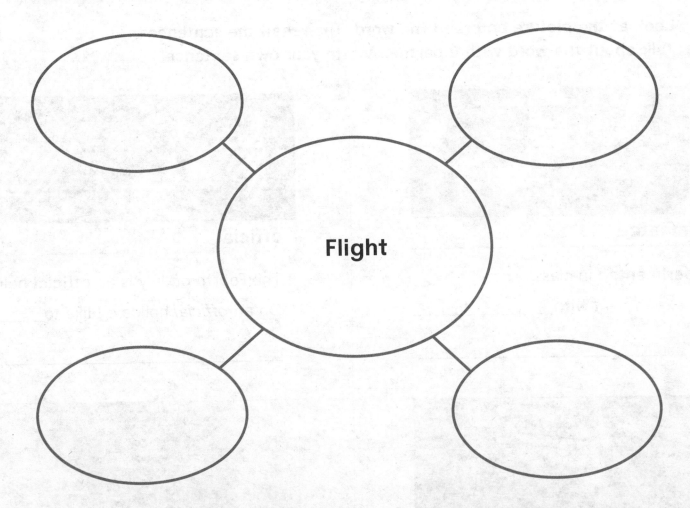

Flight

Talk about how people learned to fly. Use the words from the chart. You can say:

People studied _____ to _____.

Inventors designed _____ that had _____.

People used planes to _____.

Unimedia Images/Unimedia International/Newscom

More Vocabulary

Look at the picture and read the word. Then read the sentences.
Talk about the word with a partner. Write your own sentence.

experimented

We **experimented** in class.

I like to *experiment* with _____

_____.

official

The Fourth of July is an **official** holiday.

On an *official* holiday, I like to_____

_____.

machine

A car is a **machine** for driving.

_____ is another kind

of *machine*.

repairing

The woman is **repairing** the doorknob.

Another word for *repairing* is _____.

research

We did **research** on the computers.

I have done *research* on _____

_____.

unlocked

I **unlocked** the answer to the math problem.

Another word for *unlocked* is _____

_____.

Words and Phrases
Phrasal Verbs

give up = **stop trying**
Our coach told us not to <u>give up</u>.

started up = **turned on; set in motion**
Dad <u>started up</u> the car.

Read the sentences below. Write the phrasal verb that means the same as the underlined words.

I never <u>stop trying</u>.

I never _____.

The car's motor <u>turned on</u> right away.

The car's motor _____ right away.

>> Go Digital **Add these phrasal verbs to your New Words notebook. Write a sentence to show the meaning of each.**

1 Talk About It

Look at the photograph. Read the title. Discuss what you see. Write your ideas.

What does the title tell you?

_____

_____

_____

_____

What does the photograph show?

_____

_____

_____

_____

Take notes as you read the text.

Firsts in Flight

Essential Question

? **How are people able to fly?**

Read about how inventors learned how to fly.

ELD.PI.3.1.Ex, ELD.PI.3.1.Br, ELD.PI.3.6.Ex, ELD.PI.3.6.Br See the California Standards section.

Orville and Wilbur Wright stood on a cold, windy beach in Kitty Hawk, North Carolina. The brothers traveled a long way from their home in Dayton, Ohio to test their newest flying **machine**. Flying had been their dream since their father had given them a toy **helicopter**.

The Wright brothers owned a bicycle shop in Dayton. In addition to selling, building, and **repairing** bicycles, they built flying machines. They flew the first one in 1899. However, the winds weren't strong enough to keep the machine in motion. So they looked for a place where the winds were stronger. As a result, they chose Kitty Hawk. It was not only windy there, but the sandy beaches made for soft landings.

Orville and Wilbur Wright

On December 17, 1903, the Wright Flyer flew for 12 seconds at Kitty Hawk.

(bkgd)Transtock/SuperStock; (inset) Everett Collection/SuperStock

Text Evidence

1 Specific Vocabulary A C T

Look at the word *helicopter*. A helicopter is an aircraft with large spinning blades on top. Underline the words that tell what the helicopter caused the brothers to do.

2 Sentence Structure A C T

Reread sentence one in the second paragraph. Where was the bicycle shop? Draw a box around the words that tell you.

3 Comprehension
Cause and Effect

Look at the second paragraph. What caused the Wright brothers to choose Kitty Hawk? Use text evidence.

_____

_____

_____

_____

ELD.PI.3.6.Ex, ELD.PI.3.6.Br, ELD.PII.3.5.Ex, ELD.PII.3.5.Br See the California Standards section.

① Specific Vocabulary Ⓐ Ⓒ Ⓣ

Look at the word *successful*. Something that is successful does what you want. Underline the words that tell what was not successful.

② Comprehension

Cause and Effect

Reread the first paragraph. What happened because the Wright brothers learned a lot about flying?

_____

_____

_____

③ Sentence Structure Ⓐ Ⓒ Ⓣ

Reread the last sentence in the second paragraph. Circle the word that connects two actions. Underline the two action verbs.

Because their first flight was not **successful**, the Wright brothers learned a lot about flying. As a result, they built a better glider with bigger wings in 1900. This glider did not work very well either. The brothers did not give up. That's why they **experimented** with a new glider in 1902. Then in 1903, they built the *Wright Flyer*, their first airplane with an engine.

Flying Firsts

By December 17, the brothers were ready to test the *Wright Flyer*. Orville started up the engines to power the plane. He controlled the plane, while Wilbur watched from the ground. The Flyer was launched into the sky. The plane moved in an upward direction, and the flight lasted twelve seconds. The Wright brothers had conquered gravity and **unlocked** the secrets of flying.

Alberto Santos-Dumont was the third man in the world to fly a plane with an engine.

©Heritage Images/Corbis

Orville and Wilbur kept improving their planes, and their flights became longer. Soon, other people tried to fly airplanes.

Will It Fly?

Do an experiment on flying using paper airplanes.

Materials needed:

• pencil • paper • ruler

Directions:

1. With a partner, fold two paper airplanes. Make the wing sizes different in each plane.

2. Gently throw one plane.

3. Measure and record how far the paper plane flew.

4. Take turns throwing the plane four more times. Each time, measure and record how far it flies.

5. Repeat the experiment with the other airplane.

6. Compare the plane's flights. Then discuss what you learned about flight.

ELD.PI.3.1.Ex, ELD.PI.3.1.Br, ELD.PI.3.6.Ex, ELD.PI.3.6.Br, ELD.PII.3.2b.Ex, ELD.PII.3.2b.Br
See the California Standards section.

Alberto Santos-Dumont was an **inventor** and pilot from Brazil. In 1906, he made the first **official** flight in front of an audience. The next year, the French pilot, Henri Farman, took along a passenger in his plane. They flew for one minute and fourteen seconds.

Better Flying Machines

Because of these flights, airplane **research** became popular with inventors. Before long, better planes were traveling longer distances. In 1909, a French pilot flew an airplane across the English Channel. This plane was very different from the Wright brothers' plane. The new plane had only one long wing across its body. It looked a lot like today's airplanes.

This is what an airplane looked like in 1930.

Soon inventors began building airplanes that could carry more people. By 1920, several new companies offered passengers the chance to fly. Humans had done the impossible. They had figured out how to fly.

Make Connections

How did the Wright brothers help people fly? **ESSENTIAL QUESTION**

Tell what you know about airplanes. Discuss other ways to fly. **TEXT TO SELF**

ELD.PI.3.1.Ex, ELD.PI.3.1.Br, ELD.PI.3.6.Ex, ELD.PI.3.6.Br See the California Standards section.

Text Evidence

1 Specific Vocabulary Ⓐ Ⓒ Ⓣ

Look at the word *inventor*. An inventor is someone who designs new things. Underline what the inventor Alberto Santos-Dumont did in 1906.

2 Comprehension
Cause and Effect

Reread paragraph one and sentence one in paragraph two. What flights caused airplane research to become popular with inventors? Draw a box around the causes.

COLLABORATE

3 Talk About It

How were planes in 1920 different from the Wright brothers' plane? Write your ideas. Cite text evidence.

_____

_____

_____

Respond to the Text

Partner Discussion Work with a partner. Answer the questions. Discuss what you learned about "Firsts in Flight." Write the page numbers where you found text evidence.

How did the Wright brothers learn to fly?

The Wright brothers tested _____ in

_____.

First, they tried several _____.

Then they first flew an airplane with an engine _____.

Text Evidence

Page(s): _____

Page(s): _____

Page(s): _____

How did other inventors make flying possible?

Alberto Santos-Dumont _____.

Henri Farman _____.

Other inventors began building _____.

Text Evidence

Page(s): _____

Page(s): _____

Page(s): _____

Group Discussion Present your answers to the group. Cite text evidence to justify your thinking. Listen to and discuss the group's opinions about your answers.

Write Work with a partner. Review your notes about "Firsts in Flight." Then write your answer to the Essential Question. Use text evidence to support your answer. Use vocabulary words from this week's reading in your writing.

How did people learn to fly?

First, the Wright brothers _____

_____.

Other inventors continued to _____

_____.

Finally, people were able to _____

_____.

Share Writing Present your writing to the class. Discuss their opinions. Think about what the class has to say. Did they justify their claims? Explain why you agree or disagree with their claims.

I agree with _____ because

_____.

That's a good comment, but _____.

ELD.PI.3.1.Ex, ELD.PI.3.1.Br, ELD.PI.3.3.Ex, ELD.PI.3.3.Br, ELD.PI.3.5.Ex, ELD.PI.3.5.Br, ELD.PI.3.6.Ex, ELD.PI.3.6.Br, ELD.PI.3.9.Ex, ELD.PI.3.9.Br, ELD.PI.3.12.Br, ELD.PI.3.12.Ex See the California Standards section.

Write to Sources

pages 264–267

Mina

Take Notes About the Text I took notes on this chart to answer the question: *How did the Wright brothers help people fly? Support your answer with text evidence.*

Main Idea

The Wright brothers helped people fly by working hard to invent an airplane.

Detail

The Wright brothers built flying machines and gliders that were not successful.

Detail

In 1903, the brothers built an airplane with an engine in Kitty Hawk, North Carolina.

Detail

The plane flew for 12 seconds.

Write About the Text I used my notes to write about how the Wright brothers helped people fly.

Student Model: *Informative Text*

The Wright brothers helped people fly by working hard to make an airplane. The Wright brothers built many flying machines. They tried again and again. The machines were not successful. Then, in 1903, they built a plane with an engine. It flew for 12 seconds. Finally, the Wright brothers had discovered the secret of flying. Then other people started building airplanes. The Wright brothers' hard work helped people fly!

TALK ABOUT IT

Weekly Concept Inspiration

? **Essential Question**
How can others
inspire us?

>> Go Digital

COLLABORATE

How can the fireman inspire others? Write words that name people who inspire others in the chart. Talk about people that inspire you.

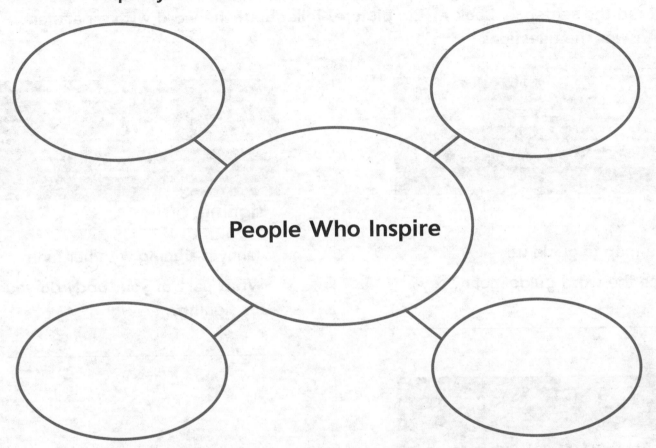

People Who Inspire

Talk about people who inspire others. Use the words from the chart. You can say:

A _____ and _____ can inspire their children

by _____.

A _____ can inspire others by being a good leader.

A _____ can inspire others when he or she _____.

More Vocabulary

COLLABORATE

Read the sentence. Look at the picture. Talk about the word with a partner. Answer the questions.

guide

We used a map to **guide** us.

What does the word *guide* mean?

_____

pale

The flowers are **pale** pink.

What is a pale color in your classroom?

_____

signing

Jenny is **signing** with her mom.

What part of your body do you use for signing?

_____

Poetry Terms

metaphor

A **metaphor** compares two things.

Jane's **fingers** are **butterflies**.

rhyme

The words *frog* and *dog* **rhyme**. They end in the same sound.

The little green **frog**.
Liked a big funny **dog**.

repetition

Repetition repeats the same word or phrase.

I won! I won!

(tl)Andrey Kekyalyaynen/Alamy; (tlr)GoranKapor/iStock/Getty Images Plus; (tr)Ariel Skelley/Blend Images LLC; (bl)Gudella/Getty Images; (br)Purestock/SuperStock

1 Sentence Structure A C T

Reread line two of the poem. An adjective is a word that describes a noun. Write the adjective that describes the noun *trips*.

_____

2 Specific Vocabulary A C T

Look at the tenth line of the poem. Circle the word *sunrise*. This compound word combines two smaller words. Draw a line separating the two words. What is a sunrise?

_____

3 Literary Element Repetition

Reread the poem. What words does the poet repeat? Draw a box around those words.

Ginger's Fingers

Ginger's fingers are shooting stars,
They talk of adventurous trips to Mars.
Fingers talking without words,
Signing when sounds can't be heard.

Ginger's fingers are ocean waves,
They talk of fish and deep sea caves.
Fingers talking without words,
Signing when sounds can't be heard.

Ginger's fingers are butterflies,
They talk of a honey-gold **sunrise**.
Fingers talking without words,
Signing when sounds can't be heard.

Essential Question

? **How can others inspire us?**

Read about different ways that people inspire others.

Diverse Images/Universal Images Group/Getty Images

ELD.PI.3.6.Ex, ELD.PI.3.6.Br, ELD.PI.3.7.Ex, ELD.PI.3.7.Br See the California Standards section.

The Giant

Dodge, dart, dash,
　　Zigzag, slash!
I sizzle, SIZZLE, when I dribble,
I'm lightning on the court.
My team calls me The Giant,
Even though I'm kinda short.

The other team might laugh to see
A player tiny as a flea.

But I'm a rocket, fiery hot,
Watch me soar, SOAR, on my jump shot!

Stretching, flexing, push, push, PUSH,
My ball flies up and in —Swoosh Woosh!

I show them all
You don't need tall
To rule the ball!

©MM Productions/Corbis

Text Evidence

❶ Literary Element
Metaphor

Read line four of the poem. What does the narrator compare himself to? Write the metaphor.

_____

❷ Comprehension
Theme

Look at the last three lines of the poem. Why does the narrator inspire others? Underline the words that tell you.

COLLABORATE

❸ Talk About It

Why does the narrator's team call him "The Giant"? Write two ways he is a giant.

_____

_____

ELD.PI.3.1.Ex, ELD.PI.3.1.Br, ELD.PI.3.6.Ex, ELD.PI.3.6.Br, ELD.PI.3.7.Ex, ELD.PI.3.7.Br
See the California Standards section.

Text Evidence

① Specific Vocabulary ⒶⒸⓉ

Look at the third line of the poem. Circle the word *satin*. Satin is a very smooth cloth. What is compared to satin in the poem?

_____

② Literary Element Repetition

A stanza in a poem is a group of lines that belong together. Reread the first stanza. Which words are repeated? Draw a box around the words.

COLLABORATE

③ Talk About It

How does the crew feel about the storm? Discuss your answers. Write your ideas.

_____

_____

_____

Captain's Log,
May 12, 1868

We set sail from a port in Spain,
Sun high, no sign of rain.
The sea was **satin**, so blue—so blue.
Our ship was a bird, we flew—we flew.

Just past noon, how very weird,
Came a sound that we most feared.
Thunder rumbled, a giant drum.
Thunder rumbled, rum tum tum.

Rain was pouring, pouring.
The wind was a monster, roaring, roaring.
My crew, extremely terrified,
Froze at their posts, **pale** and wide-eyed.

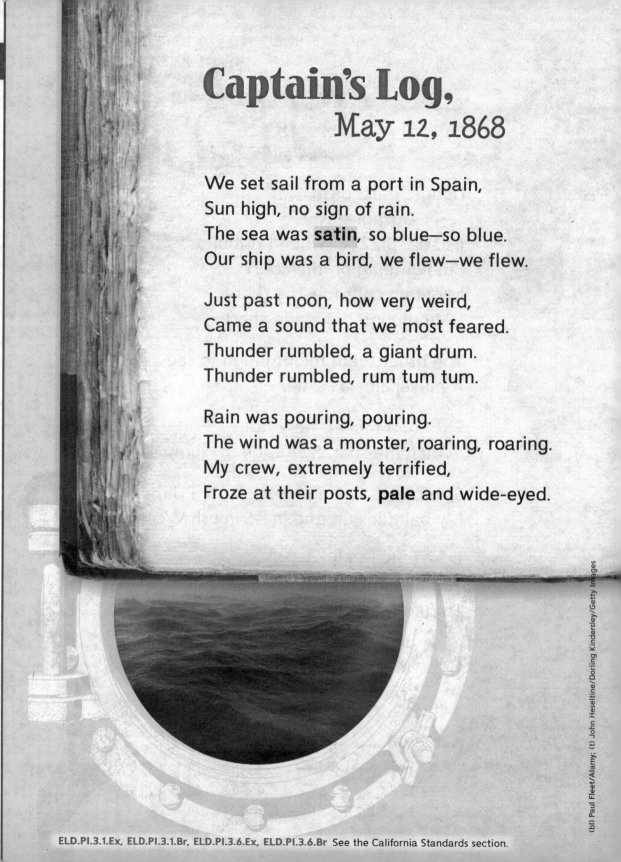

ELD.PI.3.1.Ex, ELD.PI.3.1.Br, ELD.PI.3.6.Ex, ELD.PI.3.6.Br See the California Standards section.

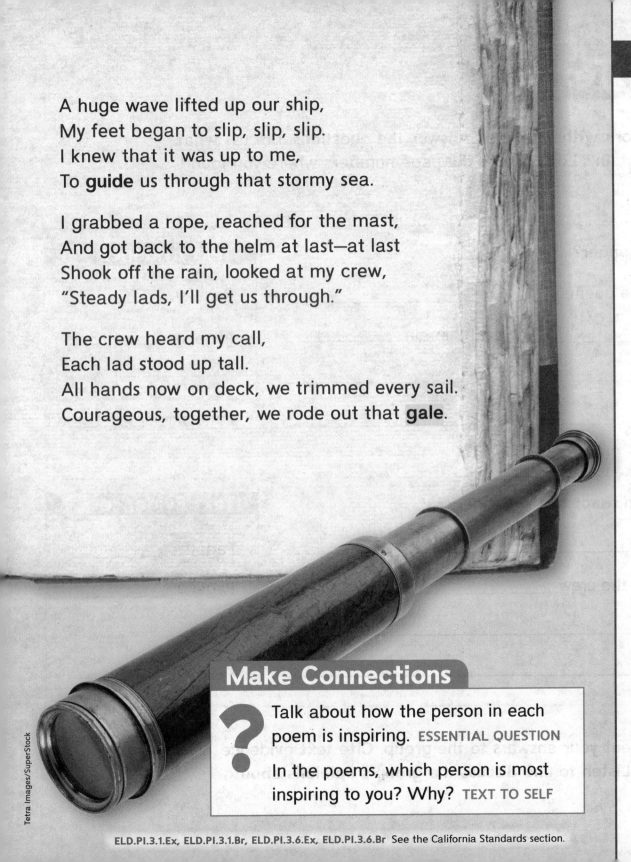

A huge wave lifted up our ship,
My feet began to slip, slip, slip.
I knew that it was up to me,
To **guide** us through that stormy sea.

I grabbed a rope, reached for the mast,
And got back to the helm at last—at last
Shook off the rain, looked at my crew,
"Steady lads, I'll get us through."

The crew heard my call,
Each lad stood up tall.
All hands now on deck, we trimmed every sail.
Courageous, together, we rode out that **gale**.

Make Connections

? Talk about how the person in each poem is inspiring. ESSENTIAL QUESTION

In the poems, which person is most inspiring to you? Why? TEXT TO SELF

Text Evidence

❶ Literary Element
Rhyme

Reread stanza five of the poem. Write two pairs of rhyming words in the stanza.

_____

_____

❷ Comprehension
Theme

Look at the last stanza. Underline the words that tell how the narrator inspires the crew.

❸ Specific Vocabulary Ⓐ Ⓒ Ⓣ

Look at the last line of the poem. A *gale* is a strong wind. What causes the gale in the poem? Write your answer.

_____

_____

_____

ELD.PI.3.1.Ex, ELD.PI.3.1.Br, ELD.PI.3.6.Ex, ELD.PI.3.6.Br See the California Standards section.

Respond to the Text

Partner Discussion Work with a partner. Answer the questions. Discuss what you learned about "Captain's Log." Write the page numbers where you found text evidence.

Why is the crew in danger?

In the beginning of the poem, _____.

Then the wind _____ and the rain _____

_____.

Large waves are _____.

Text Evidence 🔍

Page(s): _____

Page(s): _____

Page(s): _____

How does the captain react to the danger?

First, the captain gets _____.

Then the captain tells the crew _____

_____.

The crew is _____.

Text Evidence 🔍

Page(s): _____

Page(s): _____

Page(s): _____

Group Discussion Present your answers to the group. Cite text evidence to justify your thinking. Listen to and discuss the group's opinions about your answers.

280 ELD.PI.3.1.Ex, ELD.PI.3.1.Br, ELD.PI.3.3.Ex, ELD.PI.3.3.Br, ELD.PI.3.6.Ex, ELD.PI.3.6.Br See the California Standards section.

COLLABORATE

Write Review your notes about "Captain's Log." Then write your answer to the Essential Question. Use text evidence to support your answer. Use vocabulary words from this week's reading in your writing.

How does the captain in "Captain's Log" inspire his crew?

The crew feels terrified because _____

_____.

Huge waves are _____.

The captain gets _____.

He inspires the crew by _____

_____.

In the end, the captain and the crew _____.

COLLABORATE

Share Writing Present your writing to the class. Discuss their opinions. Think about what the class has to say. Did they justify their claims? Explain why you agree or disagree with their claims.

I agree with _____.

That's a good comment, but _____.

Take Notes About the Text I took notes on this idea web to answer the question: *How does the poet use metaphors in "Captain's Log"? Use one example of a metaphor from the poem in your response.*

pages 278–279

Juan

A monster is a scary creature, and roaring is a very loud noise.

I can picture the wind blowing hard and making noise.

Metaphor: The wind was a monster, roaring, roaring.

The wind is loud and scary.

It helps show why the crew is scared.

Write About the Text I used notes from my idea web to write about a metaphor in the poem "Captain's Log."

Student Model: *Informative Text*

The poet uses a metaphor in "Captain's Log" to help readers picture the storm. "The wind was a monster, roaring, roaring" is the metaphor. This metaphor compares the wind to a roaring monster. A roaring monster is a big, very loud creature. The poet uses this metaphor to show that the wind is loud and scary. The metaphor also shows why the crew is afraid. The poet's metaphor helps me picture what happens during the storm.

TALK ABOUT IT

Text Evidence

Circle the sentence that tells what a monster is. What words describe the monster?

Grammar

Underline the verb in third sentence. Is this present-tense verb an action verb?

Condense Ideas

Draw a box around the second and third sentences. How can you use the word *that* to combine these sentences?

Your Turn

How does the poet use metaphors in "Ginger's Fingers"? Use one metaphor to explain your answer.

>> *Go Digital*
Write your response online. Use your editing checklist.

UNIT
5

TAKE ACTION

THE BIG IDEA

What are ways people can take action?

COLLABORATE

What are the kids in the picture doing? How will they all get what they need? Write the words in the web.

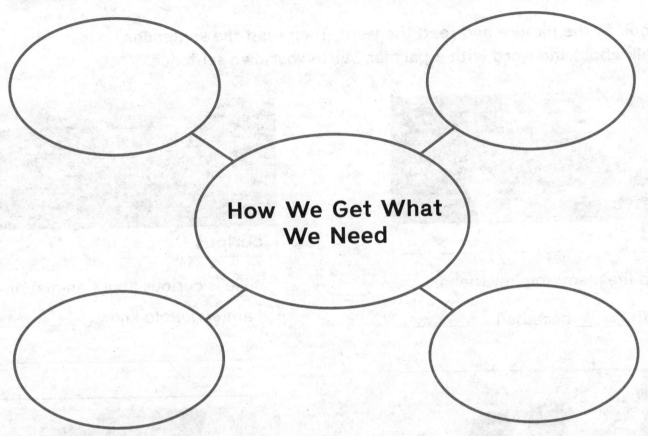

How We Get What We Need

Discuss how the kids are getting what they need. What are some different ways of getting what you need? Use the words from the web. You can say:

The kids in the picture _____ in line to get what they need.

People _____ things with money to get what they need.

People _____ things to get money.

If they don't have money, people _____ one thing

for another thing.

More Vocabulary

Look at the picture and read the word. Then read the sentences. Talk about the word with a partner. Write your own sentence.

accepted

I **accepted** the plant from my friend.

I *accepted* _____ because I _____

_____.

considerate

The **considerate** boy poured water for his grandmother.

I am *considerate* when I _____

_____.

curious

Julie is **curious** about animals in the pond.

I am *curious* to know _____

_____

_____

disobey

Our pets never **disobey** the rules.

The opposite of *disobey* is _____.

exclaimed

"We are having lots of fun!" **exclaimed** Anna.

I *exclaimed,* "_____," when I _____

_____.

trade

I will **trade** my apple for your orange.

Another word for *trade* is _____.

Words and Phrases
Verbs *get* and *get back*

get = come
I *get* home late on Mondays.

get back = receive or find something that was lost
I *was happy to* get back *my lost bike.*

Read the sentences below. Write the verb that means the same as the underlined word.

I come to school early on Fridays.

I _____ to school early on Fridays.

I will find my lost book.

I will _____ my lost book.

>> *Go Digital* Add these verbs to your New Words notebook. Write a sentence to show the meaning of *get* and *get back*.

1 Talk About It

Read the title. Discuss what you see. Write your ideas.

What do you think the title means?

_____

_____

_____

_____

_____

Where are Juanita and Mamá?

_____

_____

_____

_____

Take notes as you read the story.

Juanita and the Beanstalk

Essential Question

? How do we get what we need?

Read about what Juanita does to get what she needs.

ELD.PI.3.1.Ex, ELD.PI.3.1.Br, ELD.PI.3.6.Ex, ELD.PI.3.6.Br See the California Standards section.

Juanita lived in a small, humble **cottage** with her Mamá and her pet goat, Pepe.

One day Mamá said, "There has been no rain, and our garden has dried up. Juanita, you must go to town and sell your goat. Use the money you get as payment to buy some food."

"I don't want to sell Pepe!" cried Juanita. She petted the goat lovingly. But she was an obedient girl and would not **disobey** her mother. Reluctantly, she took Pepe to town. On her way she met an old man who patted Pepe kindly.

"He is for sale," said Juanita with tears in her eyes.

The man replied, "I have no money, but I have some special *frijoles*. If you plant these beans you will never go hungry again. We can barter, and I will **trade** you these beans for your goat."

Chris Gallo

1 Specific Vocabulary A C T

Reread the first sentence. A *cottage* is a little house. Who lives in the cottage? Circle their names.

2 Comprehension
Point of View

Reread the third and fourth paragraphs. What is Juanita's point of view about selling Pepe? Underline three pieces of text evidence that show how Juanita feels.

3 Sentence Structure A C T

Reread the first sentence of the last paragraph. The connecting word *but* contrasts two different ideas. Circle the clause that tells what the man does not have. Write what the man has.

_____

_____

ELD.PI.3.1.Ex, ELD.PI.3.1.Br, ELD.PI.3.6.Ex, ELD.PI.3.6.Br, ELD.PI.3.7.Ex, ELD.PI.3.7.Br, ELD.PI.3.8.Ex, ELD.PI.3.8.Br, ELD.PII.3.6.Ex, ELD.PII.3.6.Br See the California Standards section.

Text Evidence

1 Comprehension
Point of View

Reread the first paragraph. What is Juanita's point of view about the man? Underline the sentences that tell you.

2 Sentence Structure A C T

Reread the first sentence in the second paragraph. Circle the comma that breaks the sentence into two parts. Read each part. When is Mamá upset? Circle the sentence part that tells you.

COLLABORATE

3 Talk About It

What happens after Juanita wakes up the next morning? Take notes. Then paraphrase the events and write them below.

_____

_____

_____

Juanita thought carefully as she considered the man's offer. He seemed caring and **considerate**. Certainly he would be kind to Pepe, so Juanita finally decided to sell Pepe. She **accepted** the beans.

When Juanita got home, Mamá was upset with her decision. "You have returned home with no food and no money!" she **exclaimed**.

Juanita had to admit that Mamá was right. All she had were three beans, and she still missed Pepe. Worst of all, Mamá was unhappy.

Juanita planted the beans in the backyard and went to bed. The next morning she woke up and went outside. A gigantic beanstalk as tall as the clouds stood where Juanita had planted the beans.

Juanita was **curious**. "I'm going to see what's up there," she said to herself, so Juanita climbed the beanstalk. At the top she saw a grand and magnificent palace in the middle of a field. She knocked on the door and a maid answered.

"Hide!" cried the maid. "The giant is coming now, and he doesn't like strangers." So Juanita quickly crawled under the table.

ELD.PI.3.1.Ex, ELD.PI.3.1.Br, ELD.PI.3.6.Ex, ELD.PI.3.6.Br, ELD.PI.3.10b.Ex, ELD.PI.3.10b.Br
See the California Standards section.

The giant stomped in carrying an unhappy hen in a cage. He said, "Lay, hen, lay!" Juanita's **curiosity** grew, and she peeked from under the table. Then she saw the hen's creation. Juanita gasped. It was a golden egg!

The poor hen reminded Juanita of Pepe. She wanted to give it a better home. She ran between the giant's legs and grabbed the cage. She raced to the beanstalk. The giant roared in anger and chased after her. Juanita was able to slide down the beanstalk, but the giant was too heavy. He caused the stalk to break and crash to the ground. The beanstalk was gone forever, and Juanita and the hen were safe.

The hen was happy to have a new home and laid many golden eggs. Mamá was happy to use the eggs to buy everything they needed. And Juanita was happy because she was able to trade a golden egg with the old man to get Pepe back!

Make Connections

? How does Juanita get what she needs? ESSENTIAL QUESTION

What are some ways you can get what you need? TEXT TO SELF

ELD.PI.3.1.Ex, ELD.PI.3.1.Br, ELD.PI.3.6.Ex, ELD.PI.3.6.Br, ELD.PI.3.8.Ex, ELD.PI.3.8.Br, ELD.PII.3.6.Ex, ELD.PII.3.6.Br See the California Standards section.

Text Evidence 🔍

1 Specific Vocabulary Ⓐ Ⓒ Ⓣ

Look at the first paragraph. A person with *curiosity* wants to know about something. Why does Juanita have curiosity? Underline words that tell you.

2 Sentence Structure Ⓐ Ⓒ Ⓣ

Reread the sixth sentence of the second paragraph. Circle the comma that breaks the sentence into two parts. Box the subject in each part. Circle the verbs.

COLLABORATE

3 Talk About It

Discuss why all of the characters are happy at the end of the story. Write your answer. Use text evidence.

_____

_____

_____

293

Respond to the Text

Partner Discussion Work with a partner. Answer the questions. Discuss what you learned about "Juanita and the Beanstalk." Write the page numbers where you found text evidence.

Why does Juanita have to sell Pepe?

In the story, Mamá's garden _____.

Juanita has to sell Pepe to _____.

Then Juanita trades _____.

Text Evidence 🔍

Page(s): _____

Page(s): _____

Page(s): _____

How do the beans help Juanita get what she needs?

The beans grow _____.

In the story, Juanita climbs _____

and finds _____.

Juanita uses _____ to _____.

Text Evidence 🔍

Page(s): _____

Page(s): _____

Page(s): _____

Group Discussion Present your answers to the group. Cite text evidence to justify your thinking. Listen to and discuss the group's opinions about your answers.

Write Work with a partner. Review your notes about "Juanita and the Beanstalk." Then write your answer to the Essential Question. Use text evidence to support your answer. Use vocabulary words from this week's reading in your writing.

COLLABORATE

How does Juanita get what she needs?

Juanita trades _____.

The beans grow into a _____.

Juanita climbs _____.

Juanita finds a _____.

Mamá uses the eggs to _____.

Juanita trades an egg _____.

Share Writing Present your writing to the class. Discuss their opinions. Think about what the class has to say. Did they justify their claims? Explain why you agree or disagree with their claims. You can say:

COLLABORATE

I think your ideas are _____.

I do not agree because _____.

Write to Sources

pages 290–293

Take Notes About the Text I took notes about the story on this chart to respond to the prompt: *Add an event to the story. Write a dialogue between Juanita and Mamá at the end of the story.*

Olivia

Dialogue in the Story	
Mamá's words	"There has been no rain, and our garden has dried up. Juanita, you must go to town and sell your goat. Use the money you get as payment to buy some food."
Juanita's words	"I don't want to sell Pepe!"
Juanita's words	"I'm going to see what's up there."
Giant's words	"Lay, hen, lay!"

Write About the Text I used notes from my chart to write a dialogue between Juanita and Mamá.

Student Model: *Narrative Text*

"Mamá! I am home," called Juanita.

Mamá asked, "Where were you, Juanita?"

Juanita said, "I planted the beans, and they grew into a huge beanstalk. I climbed up and saw a mean giant. He had a hen. The hen was unhappy. The hen was in a cage. He said 'Lay, hen, lay!' So she made a golden egg! Then I took the hen. Now we can buy the things we need!"

"You were very brave," Mamá said.

TALK ABOUT IT

COLLABORATE

Text Evidence

Draw a box around the sentence that comes from the notes. Why does Olivia include this sentence in her dialogue?

Grammar

Underline the sentence about the golden egg. What does the pronoun *she* refer to?

Condense Ideas

Circle the fifth, sixth, and seventh sentences. How can you combine the sentences to connect the ideas?

Your Turn

COLLABORATE

Write a dialogue between Juanita and the old man. Show what they say when she gives him a golden egg to get Pepe back.

>> *Go Digital*
Write your response online. Use your editing checklist.

ELD.PI.3.10a.Ex, ELD.PI.3.10a.Br, ELD.PI.3.10b.Ex, ELD.PI.3.10b.Br, ELD.PII.3.1.Ex, ELD.PII.3.1.Br, ELD.PII.3.2a.Ex, ELD.PII.3.2a.Br, ELD.PII.3.6.Ex, ELD.PII.3.6.Br
See the California Standards section.

TALK ABOUT IT

Weekly Concept Reuse and Recycle

? **Essential Question**
How can we reuse what we already have?

>> *Go Digital*

298

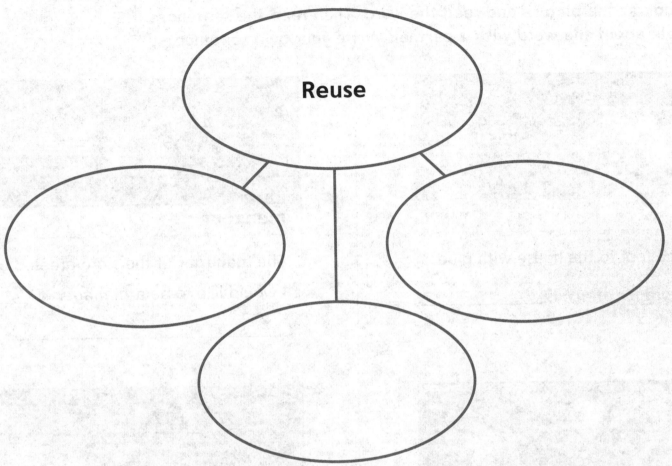

What are the kids in the picture doing? What did they reuse? What did they make? Write the words in the web.

Reuse

Discuss how the kids are reusing what they already have. What did they make from recycled things? Use the words from the web. You can say:

These kids _____ an old _____.

They hung the tire on some _____.

They made a fun _____ to use.

Bob Elsdale/Stone/Getty Images

More Vocabulary

Look at the picture and read the word. Then read the sentences.
Talk about the word with a partner. Write your own sentence.

attach

I **attach** the roof to the house with glue.

Another word for *attach* is _____.

manager

The **manager** of the store greeted us.

I would like to be a *manager* of _____

_____

containers

We keep the paint in different **containers**.

I use *containers* at home for _____

_____

materials

We use different **materials** to make a poster.

Some *materials* artists use are _____

_____

ruined

The rain **ruined** my books.

Another word for *ruined* is _____

_____.

separate

The kids have to **separate** paper from plastic.

The kids *separate* the materials so _____

_____.

Words and Phrases
Suffixes *-ful* and *-less*

The suffix *-ful* means "full of."
A pan is a <u>useful</u> tool for a cook.

The suffix *-less* means "without" or "having no."
I cleaned the window so it is <u>spotless</u>.

Read the sentences below. Write the word that means the same as the underlined words.

The baby is <u>full of cheer</u> when she wakes up.

The baby is _____ when she wakes up.

The sky has <u>no clouds</u>.

The sky is _____.

>> *Go Digital* **Add these words with suffixes to your New Words notebook. Write a sentence to show the meaning of each word.**

COLLABORATE

1 Talk About It

Read the title. Discuss what you see. Write your ideas.

What do you think the title means?

_____

_____

_____

_____

How do you think Marco and Kim will get a new hoop?

_____

_____

_____

_____

Take notes as you read the story.

The New HOOP

Essential Question

? How can we reuse what we already have?

Read to see how Kim and Marco reuse something to solve their problem.

ELD.PI.3.1.Ex, ELD.PI.3.1.Br, ELD.PI.3.6.Ex, ELD.PI.3.6.Br See the California Standards section.

Marco gazed at the basketball hoop and threw the ball up. It whizzed through the air. "Score!" he shouted as the ball fell through with a swish.

"You won this time, but I'll beat you next time, Marco!" said Kim as the two friends made their way home. "I wish we could play at home, too, instead of only at school. It's not fair." The basketball hoop in their neighborhood park had been **ruined** when a tree fell and crushed it.

"My dad says the Parks Department doesn't have enough money to buy a new hoop yet," grumbled Marco in frustration.

"I feel so discouraged," said Kim. "I guess there's nothing we can do."

Marco and Kim went past the city's recycling center. They waved at the **manager**, Mr. Morse. His job was to **separate** the plastic, paper, and metal items people brought to him. He was **transferring** cardboard from an overflowing bin into large, empty **containers**.

ELD.PI.3.1.Ex, ELD.PI.3.1.Br, ELD.PI.3.6.Ex, ELD.PI.3.6.Br, ELD.PI.3.8.Ex, ELD.PI.3.8.Br, ELD.PII.3.6.Ex, ELD.PII.3.6.Br See the California Standards section.

Text Evidence

1 Sentence Structure Ⓐ Ⓒ Ⓣ

Reread the first sentence. Underline Marco's two actions. Then circle the connecting word that joins the two actions.

COLLABORATE

2 Talk About It

How do Marco and Kim feel about the basketball hoop? Use text evidence in your answer.

_____

_____

3 Specific Vocabulary Ⓐ Ⓒ Ⓣ

Look at *transferring*. It means "moving objects from one place to another." What is Mr. Morse transferring? Draw a box around the words that tell you.

Text Evidence

1 Sentence Structure (A C T)

Reread the second sentence in the fourth paragraph. Circle the comma that separates the sentence into two clauses. What will happen after Marco and Kim cut off the bottom of the basket? Underline the clause that tells you.

2 Specific Vocabulary (A C T)

Look at the fifth paragraph. A *hand-me-down* is something that someone gives you after using it. What word in the paragraph is the opposite of hand-me-down? Circle the word.

3 Comprehension

Point of View

What is Kim's point of view about using an old laundry basket for a new basketball hoop? Cite text evidence.

Marco stared at all the old stuff. "That gives me an idea!" he said. "Mr. Morse, do you have anything we could reuse to make a basketball hoop?"

Mr. Morse picked up a plastic laundry basket. "We were going to recycle this basket, but I think it's reusable."

"It looks useless, old, and cracked," said Kim.

"No, it could be useful," said Marco. "We can cut off the bottom to make a fine hoop, and then an adult can help us **attach** it to a post."

Kim frowned. "I want a new basketball hoop," she said. "Not someone else's **hand-me-down**."

"Why?" wondered Marco. "Reusing things is a great way to practice conservation. It stops waste."

"I guess we can try," said Kim. "But I still don't believe it will be as good as a new one."

They took the basket to Marco's house. His older brother, Victor, got some leftover wood from an old building project. Together they tinkered with the **materials** and made a post and a backboard.

When Marco went to attach the basket to the backboard, he found his two cats napping in it. "I see someone has found a way to reuse the basket already!" he laughed. He let them sleep a few minutes longer.

ELD.PI.3.1.Ex, ELD.PI.3.1.Br, ELD.PI.3.6.Ex, ELD.PI.3.6.Br See the California Standards section.

When all the parts were ready, there was only one thing remaining to do. Marco, Kim, and Victor took everything to the park. Kim helped dig the hole for the post, but she was still unsure. Next, Marco helped Victor ease the post carefully into the hole.

"It looks better than I thought it would!" said Kim.

"Here's the real **test**!" grinned Marco. He tossed her the basketball. Kim bounced the ball, aimed, and shot a perfect basket. She was jubilant.

"Wow, I was wrong," she said. "This recycled basketball hoop is really great. Now we can play whenever we want!"

"Yes, and I can beat you whenever I want," grinned Marco.

"Oh, no you can't!" laughed Kim. The two friends played basketball until dinner time.

Chris Vallo

Make Connections

? What is Kim and Marco's problem? How do they reuse something to solve it? **ESSENTIAL QUESTION**

Discuss how you reused something to solve a problem. How did it work? **TEXT TO SELF**

ELD.PI.3.1.Ex, ELD.PI.3.1.Br, ELD.PI.3.6.Ex, ELD.PI.3.6.Br, ELD.PII.3.2b.Ex, ELD.PII.3.2b.Br
See the California Standards section.

Text Evidence

1 Sentence Structure Ⓐ Ⓒ Ⓣ

Reread the first paragraph. Which connecting word shows what happens after Kim helps dig the hole? Circle the word.

2 Specific Vocabulary Ⓐ Ⓒ Ⓣ

Reread the third paragraph. People *test* an object to make sure it works correctly. How does Kim do a test of the basket? Draw a box around the sentence that tells you.

COLLABORATE

3 Talk About It

How have Kim's ideas about recycling changed since the beginning of the story? Cite text evidence in your answer.

_____

_____

_____

_____

Respond to the Text

Partner Discussion Work with a partner. Answer the questions. Discuss what you learned about "The New Hoop." Write the page numbers where you found text evidence.

What is Marco and Kim's problem in the beginning?

Kim and Marco cannot play _____.

In the story, a tree fell on the basketball hoop at the _____.

Text Evidence 🔍

Page(s): _____

Page(s): _____

What do Marco and Kim do to solve their problem?

At the recycling center, Marco has _____.

Marco and Kim make a _____.

The kids learn that _____.

Text Evidence 🔍

Page(s): _____

Page(s): _____

Page(s): _____

Group Discussion Present your answers to the group. Cite text evidence to justify your thinking. Listen to and discuss the group's opinions about your answers.

Write Work with a partner. Review your notes about "The New Hoop." Then write your answer to the Essential Question. Use text evidence to support your answer. Use vocabulary words from this week's reading in your writing.

How do Marco and Kim reuse something?

Marco and Kim cannot play _____

_____.

Marco has the idea to _____

_____.

Marco, Kim, and Victor make a _____

out of _____

In the end, Marco and Kim are able to _____

_____.

Share Writing Present your writing to the class. Discuss their opinions. Think about what the class has to say. Did they justify their claims? Explain why you agree or disagree with their claims. You can say:

I think your idea is _____.

I do not agree because _____.

Write to Sources

Jayla

Take Notes About the Text I took notes about the story on this chart to respond to the prompt: *Add an event to the story. Have Kim tell her family how she and Marco made a new basketball hoop. Use sensory language.*

pages 302–305

Mr. Morse gave Marco an old, cracked, laundry basket.

↓

Victor helped make a post and backboard.

↓

Marco attached the basket to the backboard.

↓

They put the hoop up at the park.

Write About the Text I used my notes to write about
how Kim tells her family about the new basketball hoop.

Student Model: *Narrative Text*

Kim and her family were eating dinner.
Kim was excited. She said, "Marco and I
made a new basketball hoop for the park!"

Her brother asked, "How did you do
that?"

Kim explained, "Mr. Morse gave Marco
an old, cracked, laundry basket. Victor got
some old wood and he helped us make a
post and backboard. Then Marco attached
the basket. Finally, we took the hoop to the
park. We put it up. It works well!"

Kim's brother smiled. "That was a good
idea!" he said.

TALK ABOUT IT

Text Evidence
Draw a box around the sentence about Mr.
Morse. What adjectives does Jayla use to
show what the basket looked like?

Grammar
Circle the sentence about the post. Who
does the subject pronoun *he* refer to? Who
does the object pronoun *us* refer to?

Condense Ideas
Underline the sentences with the word *we*.
How can you condense these two sentences
to make one detailed sentence?

Your Turn

Have Marco tell his class about the
reused basket. Use sensory language.

>> Go Digital
Write your response online. Use your editing checklist.

ELD.PI.3.1.Ex, ELD.PI.3.1.Br, ELD.PI.3.10a.Ex, ELD.PI.3.10a.Br, ELD.PI.3.10b.Ex, ELD.PI.3.10b.Br, ELD.PII.3.2a.Ex, ELD.PII.3.2a.Br, ELD.PII.3.4.Ex, ELD.PII.3.4.Br,
ELD.PII.3.7.Ex, ELD.PII.3.7.Br See the California Standards section.

COLLABORATE

Looking at the photo, why do you think the men and the dog are working together? What can the dog do that the men cannot do? Write the words in the chart.

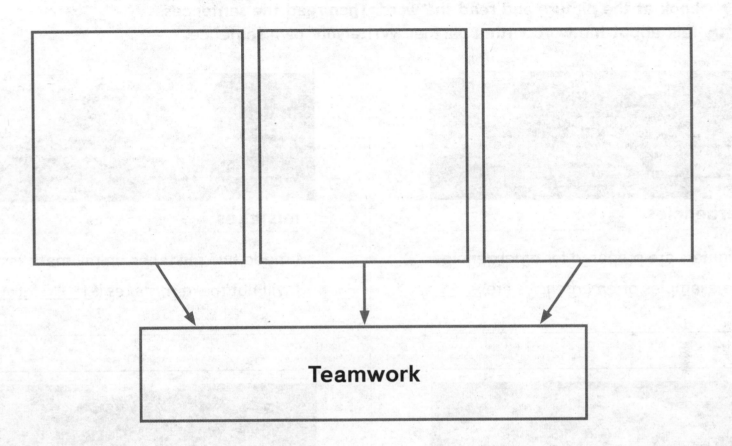

Teamwork

Discuss how the men and the dog are working together. What are they doing? Use the words from the chart.
You can say:

The men and the dog are trying to _____ something.

The dog has a better sense of _____ than the men.

The dog can _____ a hole.

ELD.PI.3.1.Ex, ELD.PI.3.1.Br, ELD.PI.3.6.Ex, ELD.PI.3.6.Br See the California Standards section.

More Vocabulary

Look at the picture and read the word. Then read the sentences. Talk about the word with a partner. Write your own sentence.

emergencies

Firefighters are prepared for **emergencies**.

Some examples of *emergencies* are _____

_____

_____.

excellent

Papa makes **excellent** empanadas.

Something is *excellent* when it is _____.

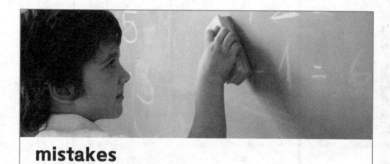

mistakes

I made two **mistakes** on my math test.

I will not make *mistakes* if I _____

_____

_____.

obedient

Jack is an **obedient** dog.

A dog is *obedient* when it _____.

training

Doing well at the sport of gymnastics takes a lot of **training**.

Another word for *training* is _____.

trust

Ella can **trust** her friend to keep a secret.

People *trust* me because _____

_____.

Words and Phrases
Multiple-Meaning Word *save*

The word *save* means to make someone safe.
A lifeguard may have to <u>save</u> a swimmer.

The word *save* means to keep money and not spend it.
I am going to <u>save</u> my money to buy a new bike.

Read the sentences below. Circle the words that mean the same as the underlined word.

Our class will <u>save</u> to buy a new computer.

make someone safe   **keep money and not spend it**

The fireman used a ladder to <u>save</u> the person.

make someone safe   **keep money and not spend it**

>> *Go Digital* Add this multiple-meaning word to your New Words notebook. Write a sentence to show each meaning of the word.

COLLABORATE

1 Talk About It

Read the title. Discuss what you see. Write your ideas.

What does the title tell you?

_____

_____

_____

What are the man and the dog doing?

_____

_____

_____

Take notes as you read the text.

Rescue Dogs
Save the Day

Essential Question

? How do teams work together?

Read how rescue dogs help in emergencies.

Rescue dogs are trained to go anywhere they are needed.

ELD.PI.3.1.Ex, ELD.PI.3.1.Br, ELD.PI.3.6.Ex, ELD.PI.3.6.Br See the California Standards section.

Rescue teams are there when we need them. They respond quickly to help people in trouble. They are brave heroes. But heroes aren't always people. Heroes can be dogs, too!

Rescue Dogs Are Heroes

Rescue dogs are always ready to go to work. They team up with police, fire and other rescue workers. They are good at finding people who are lost. They rescue families after earthquakes and other disasters. They work in all types of weather. And the best news is that rescue dogs can do their jobs with no special equipment. All they need is their **excellent** hearing and a good nose!

Rescue dogs are smart and brave. They listen well to commands and do their jobs even when they are tired, thirsty, or hungry. They are friendly and get along well with their handlers, the people who work with them. They also must be **obedient** and do what they are told.

Certain **breeds** of dogs are easier to train to work in dangerous rescue situations than others. The Border Collie is one breed of dog used during disasters and **emergencies**. Border Collies can work for a long time. They do not get tired easily, and that's important. But dogs need more than energy. They also need to follow commands, and that takes a lot of **training**.

Text Evidence

1 Comprehension

Author's Point of View

Reread the first paragraph. What is the author's point of view about rescue teams? Underline two sentences that tell what the author thinks.

2 Sentence Structure **A C T**

Look at the second paragraph. Circle the pronoun *they* each time it appears. Underline the subject in the first sentence that *they* refers to.

3 Specific Vocabulary **A C T**

Reread the first sentence in the last paragraph. There are clues in this paragraph to the meaning of *breeds*. Underline the clues. Name one breed of dog.

_____

_____

ELD.PI.3.1.Ex, ELD.PI.3.1.Br, ELD.PI.3.6.Ex, ELD.PI.3.6.Br, ELD.PI.3.7.Ex, ELD.PI.3.7.Br, ELD.PI.3.8.Ex, ELD.PI.3.8.Br, ELD.PII.3.2a.Ex, ELD.PII.3.2a.Br See the California Standards section.

Text Evidence 🔍

1 Specific Vocabulary ⒶⒸⓉ

Reread the second sentence. The word *completely* means that something has ended or is finished. How long does it take to completely train a rescue dog? Circle the words that tell you.

2 Sentence Structure ⒶⒸⓉ

Reread sentence three in the second paragraph. The word *while* connects the two clauses in the sentence. What do rescue dogs learn at the same time they are working? Underline the clause that tells you.

COLLABORATE

3 Talk About It

Discuss what rescue dogs learn to do during their training. Write two things rescue dogs do.

_____

_____

_____

316

Getting Ready to Work

Rescue dogs begin their training as puppies. It can take up to two years to **completely** train a rescue dog. Then it is able to save people in harmful and dangerous situations.

The dogs learn to work outdoors in heat, cold, and bad weather. They run, jump, and climb for many hours every day. Rescue dogs also learn to ignore everything around them while they are working. This helps them to focus on the job and keeps them from making careless **mistakes**.

Everything a rescue dog learns to do has a purpose. Even friendship is not accidental. A dog and the people it works with must learn to communicate as a team. They **trust** each other. And when they have practiced and trained enough, they are ready to participate, or take part in, a real rescue mission.

Rescue dogs are ready to dive in and help someone.

Best Rescue Dog Breeds

These dogs make great rescue dogs.				
Dog Breed	Labrador Retriever	German Shepherd	Bloodhound	Border Collie
Rescue Trait	friendly	brave	great sense of smell	lots of energy and stamina

ELD.PI.3.1.Ex, ELD.PI.3.1.Br, ELD.PI.3.6.Ex, ELD.PI.3.6.Br, ELD.PII.3.6.Ex, ELD.PII.3.6.Br
See the California Standards section.

Good Dog!

When a hiker is lost, a rescue dog sniffs the air and the ground to find her. A dog's sense of smell is much stronger than a person's. Rescue dogs can even smell someone **trapped** under fifteen feet of snow. When a dog finds someone, it barks to alert its partner. The rescue worker trusts the dog, so the team works quickly to save a life. At the end of every rescue, the dog gets praise and treats for doing a great job.

Sometimes rescue teams go to schools to teach children about safety and disaster prevention. They show children how to stay safe and what to do during emergencies. This job is fun for rescue dogs. They get lots of attention for just doing what they do best – helping people. Rescue dogs really are heroes!

This team works on snowy mountains.

Tom Bear/Aurora/Getty Images

Make Connections

? How do rescue workers and dogs work together in an emergency? **ESSENTIAL QUESTION**

What do you think is the best thing about working with a rescue dog? **TEXT TO SELF**

ELD.PI.3.1.Ex, ELD.PI.3.1.Br, ELD.PI.3.6.Ex, ELD.PI.3.6.Br, ELD.PI.3.7.Ex, ELD.PI.3.7.Br
See the California Standards section.

Text Evidence

1 Specific Vocabulary Ⓐ Ⓒ Ⓣ

Reread the third sentence in the first paragraph. A *trapped* person cannot move or get free. Circle the words that help you understand the meaning of trapped.

2 Sentence Structure Ⓐ Ⓒ Ⓣ

Reread the fourth sentence in the first paragraph. Circle the comma that breaks the sentence into two parts. Underline what a dog does when it finds someone.

3 Comprehension

Author's Point of View

Reread the last paragraph. What is the author's point of view about rescue teams visiting schools? Underline a sentence that tells what the author thinks.

317

Respond to the Text

COLLABORATE

Partner Discussion Work with a partner. Answer the questions. Discuss what you learned about "Rescue Dogs Save the Day." Write the page numbers where you found text evidence.

How do handlers train rescue dogs?

In the text, rescue dogs learn to _____.
Page(s): _____

For many hours a day, dogs _____.
Page(s): _____

The author says dogs learn to communicate _____.
Page(s): _____

Text Evidence 🔍

Why are dogs part of rescue teams?

I read that Border collies _____.
Page(s): _____

According to the author, dogs can smell _____.
Page(s): _____

Based on the text, rescue dogs alert _____.
Page(s): _____

I read that rescue teams go to schools to _____.
Page(s): _____

Text Evidence 🔍

COLLABORATE

Group Discussion Present your answers to the group. Cite text evidence to justify your thinking. Listen to and discuss the group's opinions about your answers.

ELD.PI.3.1.Ex, ELD.PI.3.1.Br, ELD.PI.3.5.Ex, ELD.PI.3.5.Br, ELD.PI.3.6.Ex, ELD.PI.3.6.Br, ELD.PI.3.12.Ex, ELD.PI.3.12.Br See the California Standards section.

Write Work with a partner. Review your notes about "Rescue Dogs Save the Day." Then write your answer to the Essential Question. Use text evidence to support your answer. Use vocabulary words from this week's reading in your writing.

How do rescue dogs and their handlers work together?

Handlers train rescue dogs _____

_____ .

Rescue dogs communicate with _____

_____ .

When a rescue dog finds someone who's trapped, _____

_____ .

Rescue dogs and their partners visit _____

_____ .

Share Writing Present your writing to the class. Discuss their opinions. Think about what the class has to say. Did they justify their claims? Explain why you agree or disagree with their claims.

I think your idea is _____ .

I do not agree because _____ .

ELD.PI.3.1.Ex, ELD.PI.3.1.Br, ELD.PI.3.3.Ex, ELD.PI.3.3.Br, ELD.PI.3.5.Ex, ELD.PI.3.5.Br, ELD.PI.3.9.Ex, ELD.PI.3.9.Br, ELD.PI.3.10b.Ex, ELD.PI.3.10b.Br, ELD.PI.3.11.Ex, ELD.PI.3.11.Br, ELD.PI.3.12.Ex, ELD.PI.3.12.Br See the California Standards section.

Write to Sources

pages 314–317

Take Notes About the Text I took notes about the text on this idea web to answer the question: *How do rescue workers and dogs work together to find lost people? Use text evidence to support your answer.*

Sebastián

First, the dog sniffs the air and ground to find the person.

The dog barks to tell the rescue worker it found the person.

How rescue workers and dogs work together

The rescue worker helps the person.

The dog gets praise and treats at the end of the rescue.

Write About the Text I used notes to write a paragraph that tells how rescue workers and dogs work together.

Student Model: *Informative Text*

Rescue workers and dogs work together. They save people who are lost. First, the dog sniffs the air and ground. When the dog smells the person, it barks. The rescue worker knows the dog has found the person. Then the rescue worker helps the person. At the end of the rescue, the dog gets praise and treats. The rescue team does a great job of finding lost people!

TALK ABOUT IT

COLLABORATE

Text Evidence
Underline the sentence about where the dog sniffs. How does the sentence help make a strong paragraph?

Grammar
Draw a box around the pronoun *it*. What noun does *it* refer to? **Draw an arrow** from *it* to the noun.

Condense Ideas
Circle the first two sentences. How can you combine the sentences to condense ideas?

Your Turn

COLLABORATE

What do rescue dogs learn in their training as puppies? Use details from the text in your answer.

>> *Go Digital*
Write your response online. Use your editing checklist.

TALK ABOUT IT

Weekly Concept Good Citizens

? Essential Question
What do good citizens do?

>> *Go Digital*

322

COLLABORATE

Why do we display the American flag? What does it show? Write the words in the web.

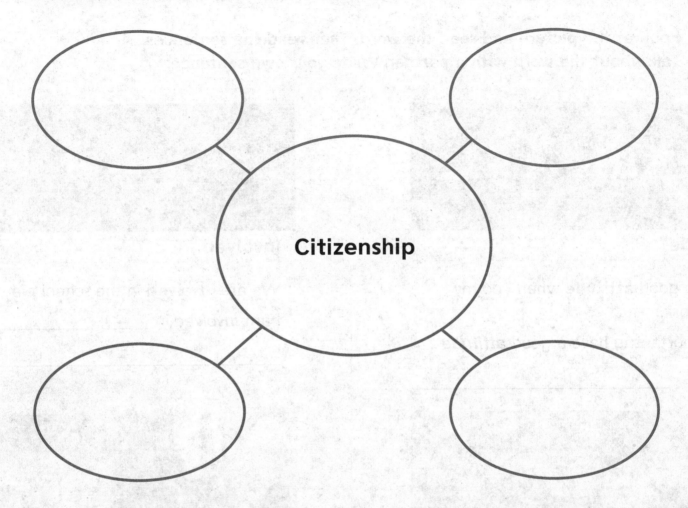

Citizenship

Discuss why the boy is planting the flag in the ground. Use the words from the web. You can say:

The boy feels _____ for his _____.

He is _____ soldiers who have served the country.

He is showing his _____.

David L. Moore–Oahu/Alamy

More Vocabulary

Look at the picture and read the word. Then read the sentences. Talk about the word with a partner. Write your own sentence.

attitude

I have a good **attitude** when I do my homework.

It is important to have a good *attitude*

because _____.

improved

My playing **improved** because I practiced.

My grades *improved* when I _____

_____.

involved

We are **involved** in the school play.

I am *involved* in _____

_____.

rights

We have a **right** to give our opinion.

Students have *rights* in my school, such as

_____.

risked

The firefighters **risked** their safety.

Rescue workers *risk* _____

when they _____.

organizations

Some **organizations** build houses for people.

I want to join an *organization* that _____

_____.

Words and Phrases
Multiple-Meaning Word *hard*

The word *hard* means "not soft."
I sat on a <u>hard</u> chair.

The word *hard* means "using a lot of effort."
Washing dishes is a <u>hard</u> job.

Read the sentences below. Circle the words that mean the same as the underlined word.

He scraped his knee on the <u>hard</u> ground.

not soft   using much effort

Building a house is <u>hard</u> work.

not soft   using much effort

>> *Go Digital* Add this multiple-meaning word to your New Words notebook. Write a sentence to show each meaning of the word *hard*.

COLLABORATE

1 Talk About It

Read the title. Discuss what you see. Write your ideas.

Why do you think Dolores Huerta is strong?

_____

_____

_____

_____

Where does Dolores Huerta work?

_____

_____

_____

_____

Take notes as you read the text.

Dolores Huerta
GROWING UP STRONG

Essential Question

? **What do good citizens do?**

Read how Dolores Huerta's actions helped many people.

ELD.PI.3.1.Ex, ELD.PI.3.1.Br, ELD.PI.3.6.Ex, ELD.PI.3.6.Br See the California Standards section.

Dolores Huerta learned to help people by watching her mother. Good citizenship was important to her, and she taught Dolores that women can be strong leaders. When Dolores grew up, she had the same beliefs.

Good Citizens

Dolores was born on April 10, 1930. She lived in a small town in New Mexico until she was three years old. Then she moved to California with her mother and two brothers. Dolores grew up watching her mother participate in community **organizations**. Her mother believed that all people deserved to be treated fairly.

When Dolores was a young girl, her mother owned a hotel and a restaurant. Many farm workers who lived in their town were poor and hungry. They were paid very little for their hard work. Dolores's mother let them stay at her hotel and eat at her restaurant for free. This taught Dolores and her brothers that good citizens get **involved** in the community by helping their **neighbors**.

Dolores Huerta helped farm workers who spent many hours working in fields.

Dr. Parvinder Sethi

❶ Sentence Structure Ⓐ Ⓒ Ⓣ

Reread the second sentence. Circle the comma that breaks the compound sentence into two parts. Box the word that connects each part of the sentence. Underline the part that tells what was important.

❷ Specific Vocabulary Ⓐ Ⓒ Ⓣ

Reread the last sentence. A *neighbor* is someone who lives close. Who were Dolores's neighbors? Circle the words that tell you.

COLLABORATE

❸ Talk About It

How do you know that Dolores's mother was a good citizen? Justify your answer.

_____

_____

_____

ELD.PI.3.1.Ex, ELD.PI.3.1.Br, ELD.PI.3.6.Ex, ELD.PI.3.6.Br, ELD.PII.3.6.Ex, ELD.PII.3.6.Br
See the California Standards section.

327

Text Evidence

1 Specific Vocabulary Ⓐ Ⓒ Ⓣ

The word *attended* means "went to classes in school." Circle what Dolores attended.

2 Sentence Structure Ⓐ Ⓒ Ⓣ

Reread sentence three in the second paragraph. Circle the word that connects the two clauses in the sentence. Which clause explains why students came to school barefoot? Underline the clause.

3 Comprehension

Author's Point of View

Reread the last paragraph. What is the author's point of view about Dolores helping children of farm workers? Underline two sentences that tell what the author thinks.

Dolores Goes to School

Dolores saw how hard life was for farm workers in California. She wanted everyone to be treated fairly. This **attitude** continued as she **attended** college and studied to become a teacher.

Many of the students that Dolores taught were the children of farm workers. These students were often tired and hungry. They came to school barefoot because they had no shoes. Dolores knew she needed to help them. As a result, she went to her school's principal and proposed some good ideas. She tried to get free lunches and milk for the children. She tried to get them new clothes and shoes.

Trying to help the children was a daring thing for Dolores to do. The other teachers did not agree with her ideas. Dolores **risked** a lot, but her beliefs did not waver. She decided to do something about the unfairness she saw. She wanted to find a better way to help farm workers and their families.

Arthur Schatz/Time & Life Pictures/Getty Images

Dolores: Strong and Fair

This time line shows important dates in Dolores Huerta's life.

1930	1940	1950	1960	1970	1980

1933: Moved to California

1953–1955: Worked as a teacher

1955: Met César Chávez

1930: Dolores is born

1962: Dolores and César started National Farm Workers Association

1975: Helped pass laws to protect farm workers

ELD.PI.3.1.Ex, ELD.PI.3.1.Br, ELD.PI.3.6.Ex, ELD.PI.3.6.Br, ELD.PII.3.6.Ex, ELD.PII.3.6.Br
See the California Standards section.

Dolores Stands Strong

Every day Dolores saw people working in unusually **unsafe** and disagreeable conditions. She was horrified. Many farm workers had little money to feed their families. Dolores decided to do something.

In 1955, Dolores met César Chávez. He wanted to make life better for farm workers, too. Dolores and César organized the workers into a group called the National Farm Workers Association. This group protected the **rights** of the farm workers. It helped make big farms treat them better. As a result, working conditions on the farms **improved**.

Growing up with a mother who cared about other people taught Dolores to be a good citizen. Her kind and brave acts helped farm workers and their families. Who is a good citizen? Dolores Huerta is!

Dolores Huerta speaks for farm workers at a rally in 1969.

1990   2000   2010

1998:
Earned Human Rights Award from President Clinton

Make Connections

How did Dolores Huerta's actions make her a good citizen? **ESSENTIAL QUESTION**

What can you do to improve people's lives? **TEXT TO SELF**

ELD.PI.3.1.Ex, ELD.PI.3.1.Br, ELD.PI.3.6.Ex, ELD.PI.3.6.Br, ELD.PII.3.4.Ex, ELD.PII.3.4.Br
See the California Standards section.

Text Evidence

1 Specific Vocabulary Ⓐ Ⓒ Ⓣ

Reread sentence one in the first paragraph. Something that is *unsafe* is dangerous. Why were people unsafe?

_____

_____

2 Sentence Structure Ⓐ Ⓒ Ⓣ

Look at the first sentence in the last paragraph. Underline the clause "who cared about other people." What noun does this clause describe? Circle the noun.

COLLABORATE

3 Talk About It

Why were Dolores and César Chávez a good team? Use text evidence in your answer.

_____

_____

_____

329

Respond to the Text

Partner Discussion Work with a partner. Answer the questions. Discuss what you learned about "Dolores Huerta: Growing Up Strong." Write the page numbers where you found text evidence.

What did Dolores learn from her mother?

Text Evidence 🔍

I read that Dolores's mother believed _____.

Page(s): _____

Dolores's mother let farm workers _____.

Page(s): _____

In the text, Dolores learned from her mother that _____

_____.

Page(s): _____

How did Dolores help farm workers and their families?

Text Evidence 🔍

In the text, Dolores wanted to get farm workers' children _____.

Page(s): _____

I read that Dolores and César Chávez formed _____.

Page(s): _____

Big farms treated farm workers better because _____.

Page(s): _____

COLLABORATE

Group Discussion Present your answers to the group. Cite text evidence to justify your thinking. Listen to and discuss the group's opinions about your answers.

ELD.PI.3.1.Ex, ELD.PI.3.1.Br, ELD.PI.3.5.Ex, ELD.PI.3.5.Br, ELD.PI.3.6.Ex, ELD.PI.3.6.Br, ELD.PI.3.9.Ex, ELD.PI.3.9.Br, ELD.PI.3.12.Ex, ELD.PI.3.12.Br
See the California Standards section.

Write Work with a partner. Review your notes about "Dolores Huerta: Growing Up Strong." Then write your answer to the Essential Question. Use text evidence to support your answer. Use vocabulary words from this week's reading in your writing.

COLLABORATE

What did Dolores Huerta do to be a good citizen?

When Dolores was a teacher, she _____

_____.

When Dolores saw farm workers working in _____

_____.

Dolores and César Chávez formed _____

_____.

Dolores and César helped make big farms _____

_____.

Share Writing Present your writing to the class. Discuss their opinions. Think about what the class has to say. Did they justify their claims? Explain why you agree or disagree with their claims.

COLLABORATE

I think your idea is _____.

I do not agree because _____.

Write to Sources

pages 326–329

Take Notes About the Text I took notes on this idea web to answer the question: *Why does the author use Dolores Huerta as an example of a good citizen?*

Camilla

Dolores's students were hungry and had no shoes.

Dolores tried to get shoes and food for her students.

The author uses Dolores Huerta as an example of a good citizen.

Many farm workers were not treated fairly by big farms.

Dolores and César Chávez helped make big farms treat workers better.

Write About the Text I used my notes to write about why Dolores Huerta is an example of a good citizen.

Student Model: *Informative Text*

The author uses Dolores Huerta as an example of a good citizen because she helped others. She wanted everyone to be treated fairly. Dolores was a teacher. Her students were hungry and had no shoes. She tried to get shoes and food for them.

Later, Dolores worked with César Chávez to help farm workers. The farm workers were not treated fairly. Dolores and César helped make big farms treat the workers better. Dolores Huerta is a good citizen because she helped many people.

TALK ABOUT IT
COLLABORATE

Text Evidence
Underline the first sentence. **Circle** what a good citizen does. Why is this sentence a strong opening?

Grammar
Draw a box around the sentence that describes the students. What noun does the possessive pronoun *her* refer to?

Condense Ideas
Circle the first two sentences about farm workers. How can you use the word *who* to combine the sentences?

Your Turn
COLLABORATE

How does the time line support the author's point of view that Dolores Huerta is a good citizen?

>> *Go Digital*
Write your response online. Use your editing checklist.

ELD.PI.3.10a.Ex, ELD.PI.3.10a.Br, ELD.PI.3.10b.Ex, ELD.PI.3.10b.Br, ELD.PII.3.1.Ex, ELD.PII.3.1.Br, ELD.PII.3.2a.Ex, ELD.PII.3.2a.Br, ELD.PII.3.7.Ex, ELD.PII.3.7.Br
See the California Standards section.

? **Essential Question**

What are different kinds of energy?

>> *Go Digital*

What is the boy in the picture doing? How does he get his energy? Look at the windmills in the picture. How do they get their energy? Write the words in the web.

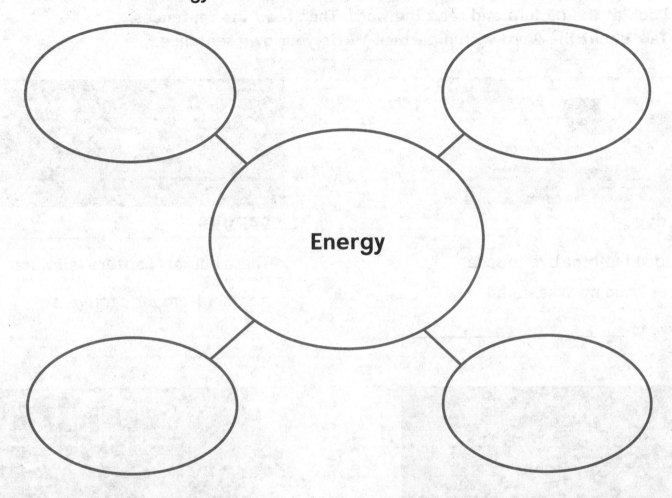

Energy

Discuss how the boy gets his energy. Discuss how the windmills get their energy. Use the words from the web. You can say:

Eating many _____ gives this boy _____.

_____ is a _____ of energy for windmills.

ELD.PI.3.1.Ex, ELD.PI.3.1.Br, ELD.PI.3.6.Ex, ELD.PI.3.6.Br See the California Standards section.

More Vocabulary

COLLABORATE

Look at the picture and read the word. Then read the sentences. Talk about the word with a partner. Write your own sentence.

alternative

Milk is a good **alternative** to soda.

Sometimes I ride my bike, as an

alternative to _____.

capture

These buckets **capture** rainwater.

Another word for *capture* is _____.

available

Only four seats are **available**.

If something is *available*, it is _____.

expensive

The fire department bought an **expensive** new fire truck.

Yesterday, I bought an *expensive* _____.

flows

The water **flows** quickly over the rocks.

The water in the sink *flows* _____

_____.

surface

We skate on the ice's smooth **surface**.

Years ago, astronauts landed on the

surface of the _____.

Words and Phrases
Phrasal Verbs *turn on* and *turn to*

To *turn on* means to make something work by pushing a button or flipping a switch.
I will <u>turn on</u> a light so I can read.

To *turn to* means to do something new or different.
Ben <u>turned to</u> reading because he could not go to the park.

Read the sentences below. Write the phrasal verb that means the same as the underlined words.

Jan <u>did something new by</u> knitting after she hurt her knee.

turned on   turned to

I will <u>push the button on</u> the TV and watch a show.

turn on   turn to

>> *Go Digital*   Add these phrasal verbs to your New Words notebook. Write a sentence to show the meaning of each.

COLLABORATE

1 Talk About It

Read the title. Discuss what you see. Write your ideas.

What does the title tell you?

_____

_____

_____

_____

What is the boy doing?

_____

_____

_____

Why is solar power important to

the boy? _____

_____

Take notes as you read the text.

This snowboarder gets his power from the healthful foods he eats.

Essential Question

? **What are different kinds of energy?**

Read why solar energy is a good source of power.

ELD.PI.3.1.Ex, ELD.PI.3.1.Br, ELD.PI.3.6.Ex, ELD.PI.3.6.Br See the California Standards section.

Here Comes Solar Power

What do you have **in common** with a car and a factory? You both need energy to run. Energy keeps things moving.

Energy Today

You get your energy from eating healthful foods. Most factories, homes, and cars get their energy from fossil fuels. Coal, petroleum, and natural gas are fossil fuels. They have been the traditional, or usual, energy sources for more than a century. Today, most of the energy we use in the United States comes from burning fossil fuels.

But these fuels come from deep under the Earth's **surface**, and they are running out. They cannot be reused. Once a fossil fuel is gone, it's gone forever. So we need **alternative** energy sources to replace them. Scientists know that there is no other way to keep our country going and growing. So they are looking for new, alternative sources of energy that won't run out.

ELD.PI.3.1.Ex, ELD.PI.3.1.Br, ELD.PI.3.6.Ex, ELD.PI.3.6.Br, ELD.PII.3.1.Ex, ELD.PII.3.1.Br
See the California Standards section.

Text Evidence

1 Specific Vocabulary A C T

Reread the question in the first paragraph. The phrase *in common* means something that two things share. What do you have in common with a car?

_____

_____

2 Sentence Structure A C T

Reread the third sentence of the second paragraph. Circle the commas that separate the fossil fuels. Underline the name of each fossil fuel.

3 Comprehension

Cause and Effect

Look at the last paragraph. Why should we replace fossil fuels?

_____

_____

_____

1 Sentence Structure A C T

Reread the last sentence in the first paragraph. Circle the connecting word that joins the two ideas about solar panels. Underline each idea.

2 Comprehension

Cause and Effect

Reread the second paragraph. What happens when electricity flows into a building? Circle the connecting word that signals what happens. Underline what happens.

3 Specific Vocabulary A C T

Reread the first sentence in the third paragraph. A *company* is a large business. Why is it important for companies to turn to solar power?

_____

_____

Cheaper and Cleaner

Solar power is one source of renewable energy. And it is not **expensive**. As a result, many people are placing solar panels on the roofs of homes and large buildings. Solar panels look like giant mirrors, and they **capture** energy from the Sun.

On a bright day, the Sun's rays hit the solar panel and cause it to produce electricity. Then the electricity **flows** into the building. As a result, there is enough energy to raise the temperature inside homes, and turn on lights, stoves, and computers.

The Future

More **companies** are turning to solar power to replace fossil fuels. It's natural. That means it isn't made, or changed, by people. Solar power is cheaper than fossil fuels, and it does not create pollution.

Today there are millions of people around the world using solar power to produce electricity for their homes and businesses. Someday solar power may completely replace fossil fuels.

Solar panels are placed on the roofs of buildings.

ELD.PI.3.1.Ex, ELD.PI.3.1.Br, ELD.PI.3.6.Ex, ELD.PI.3.6.Br, ELD.PII.3.1.Ex, ELD.PII.3.1.Br, ELD.PII.3.2b.Ex, ELD.PII.3.2b.Br, ELD.PII.3.6.Ex, ELD.PII.3.6.Br See the California Standards section.

GO SUNSHINE!

Renewable energy is **where it's at**. And solar power is at the top of our list. Here are the top reasons why solar energy is so hot!

• Solar power is cheaper than fossil fuels.

• It is renewable.

• It doesn't cause pollution and is good for our environment.

• Power from the Sun is always **available**.

• Solar power is natural.

Solar energy can do just about everything that fossil fuels do. Everyone should use solar power. It's good news for the planet!

Thanks to solar power, Paul can power up and listen to his MP3 player.

Make Connections

? Why is solar power a good source of energy? ESSENTIAL QUESTION

What are some ways you might use solar power? TEXT TO SELF

Text Evidence

1 Specific Vocabulary A C T

Reread the first sentence. *Where it's at* is an idiom people use in conversations. "Where it's at" means "popular." Circle the phrases in the second and third sentences that also mean something is popular or well-liked.

COLLABORATE

2 Talk About It

Discuss the author's opinion about solar power. Find text evidence to support that opinion. Do you agree or disagree? Support your idea.

_____

_____

_____

_____

_____

_____

_____

ELD.PI.3.1.Ex, ELD.PI.3.1.Br, ELD.PI.3.3.Ex, ELD.PI.3.3.Br ELD.PI.3.6.Ex, ELD.PI.3.6.Br, ELD.PI.3.7.Ex, ELD.PI.3.7.Br, ELD.PI.3.8.Ex, ELD.PI.3.8.Br, ELD.PI.3.11.Ex, ELD.PI.3.11.Br See the California Standards section.

341

Partner Discussion Work with a partner. Answer the questions. Discuss what you learned about "Here Comes Solar Power." Write the page numbers where you found text evidence.

Where does most of our energy come from?

I read that traditional sources of energy are _____.

Text Evidence 🔍

Page(s): _____

In the text, fossil fuels come from _____.

Page(s): _____

Fossil fuels cannot be _____ and are

Page(s): _____

_____.

Why is solar power a good source of energy?

Solar energy is a good energy source because _____

Text Evidence 🔍

Page(s): _____

_____.

I read that solar energy is popular because _____.

Page(s): _____

Group Discussion Present your answers to the group. Cite text evidence to justify your thinking. Listen to and discuss the group's opinions about your answers.

Write Work with a partner. Review your notes about "Here Comes Solar Power." Then write your answer to the Essential Question. Use text evidence to support your answer. Use vocabulary words from this week's reading in your writing.

Why is solar energy a good power source?

Today, most energy comes from _____

_____.

We need renewable energy sources because _____

_____.

Solar power is a good renewable energy source because _____

_____.

Someday solar power may replace _____

_____.

Share Writing Present your writing to the class. Discuss their opinions. Think about what the class has to say. Did they justify their claims? Explain why you agree or disagree with their claims.

I think your idea is _____.

I do not agree because _____.

Write to Sources

pages 338–341

William

Take Notes About the Text I took notes on this idea web to answer the question: *What is your opinion about solar power? Use text evidence to support your answer.*

Solar energy never runs out.

Solar power is not expensive.

Solar power is a great thing for people and the planet.

Solar power does not make pollution.

Fossil fuels hurt the Earth.

Angela Lumsden/Moment/Getty Images

Write About the Text I used notes from my idea web to write an opinion about solar power.

Student Model: *Opinion*

I think solar power is great for people and our planet. Today we use a lot of fossil fuels. Solar energy is better. It comes from the Sun so it never runs out. In addition, solar power is not expensive. It helps people save money. And there is one more reason to use solar power. Solar power does not make pollution. I think that we should stop using fossil fuels and use solar power instead.

TALK ABOUT IT
COLLABORATE

Text Evidence
Circle the sentence about pollution. How does it help support William's opinion?

Grammar
Draw a box around the seventh sentence. How can you add the adjective *excellent* to describe the reason?

Connect Ideas
Underline the fifth and sixth sentences. How can you combine the sentences to connect the ideas?

Your Turn
COLLABORATE

Does the author do a good job of convincing readers to support solar power? Use details from the text.

>> Go Digital
Write your response online. Use your editing checklist.

Unit 6

Think It Over

The Big Idea

How do we decide what's important?

TALK ABOUT IT

Weekly Concept Treasures

? Essential Question

How do you decide
what's important?

>> *Go Digital*

What is the girl in the picture doing? What do you think is important to her? Write the words in the web.

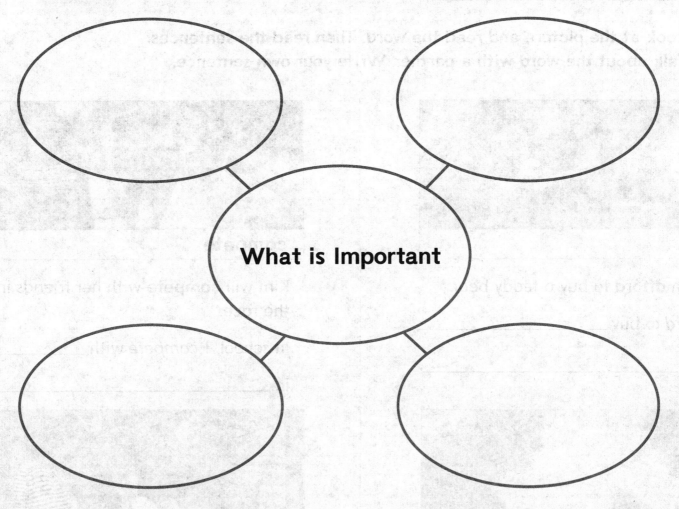

What is Important

Discuss what the girl and her grandfather are doing. Discuss what is important to her. Use the words from the web. You can say:

The girl enjoys _____ with her _____.

Spending time with _____ and _____

is important to her.

ELD.PI.3.1.Ex, ELD.PI.3.1.Br, ELD.PI.3.6.Ex, ELD.PI.3.6.Br See the California Standards section.

COLLABORATE

Look at the picture and read the word. Then read the sentences. Talk about the word with a partner. Write your own sentence.

afford

Donna can **afford** to buy a teddy bear.

I can *afford* to buy _____

_____ .

compete

Kim will **compete** with her friends in the race.

In school, I *compete* with _____

in _____ .

challenged

I **challenged** Dad to a chess match.

I would like to *challenge* _____

to _____ .

messenger

The **messenger** brought the letter to Mom.

I get very excited when a *messenger*

brings _____ .

(ul)Blend Images/Ariel Skelley/Getty Images; (ur)GoGo Images/Alamy; (bl)Mark Bowden/E+/Getty Images; (br)Peopleimages/E+/Getty Images

possession

This baseball is Sal's favorite **possession**.

My favorite *possession* is _____

_____.

value

My mom **values** this family quilt.

I *value* _____

because _____

_____.

Words and Phrases
Homographs *rest*

rest = what is left
We will save the <u>rest</u> of the pizza for later.

rest = stop working and relax
Dad will <u>rest</u> after mowing the lawn.

Read the sentences below. Circle the words that mean the same as the underlined words.

The runners will <u>rest</u> after the race.

what is left   stop working and relax

I gave the <u>rest</u> of my sandwich to the dog.

what is left   stop working and relax

>> *Go Digital* Add the homograph *rest* to your New Words notebook. Write sentences to show each meaning of the word.

(t)Rob Friedman/E+/Getty Images; (b)Willard/iStock/Getty Images Plus

COLLABORATE

❶ Talk About It

Read the title. Discuss what you see. Write your ideas.

Who are the main characters in the drama?

_____

_____

_____

_____

What are the women doing in this picture?

_____

_____

_____

Take notes as you read the drama.

ATHENA AND ARACHNE

Essential Question

? **How do you decide what's important?**

Read a myth that shows why valuing a talent can cause problems.

ELD.PI.3.1.Ex, ELD.PI.3.1.Br, ELD.PI.3.6.Ex, ELD.PI.3.6.Br, ELD.PI.3.12.Ex, ELD.PI.3.12.Br
See the California Standards section.

CHARACTERS

NARRATOR

ARACHNE (uh-RAK-nee)

DIANA

ATHENA

MESSENGER

⇌ SCENE ONE ⇌

Athens, Greece, a long time ago, Arachne's home.

NARRATOR: Long ago, Arachne and her friend Diana sat weaving.

DIANA: Oh, Arachne! That cloth is so beautiful.

Arachne admires her cloth.

ARACHNE: I know. Many people want to possess my cloth, but few can **afford** it. Only those with great wealth can buy it.

DIANA: Yes, it's true that people **value** your cloth. It is one of their most valued **possessions**. Your weavings are a real treasure. Some say that you learned your weaving skill, or **talent**, from the goddess Athena.

ARACHNE: It was not necessary for me to learn from a goddess. I was born with my talent. I am a much better weaver than Athena, and I'm sure I could beat her in a weaving competition!

Diana is worried, stops weaving and looks at Arachne.

DIANA: Ssshhh! I hope Athena isn't listening, or you're in big trouble!

ARACHNE: Nonsense! There's no reason to be alarmed or worried. Athena is much too busy to come down from Mount Olympus to **compete** with me.

Jenny Reynish

Text Evidence 🔍

❶ Sentence Structure Ⓐ Ⓒ Ⓣ

Reread the second sentence in Arachne's first speech. Circle the word that connects the two clauses. Underline the subject of the second clause.

❷ Specific Vocabulary Ⓐ Ⓒ Ⓣ

Reread the last sentence in Diana's second speech. What word in the sentence is a synonym for the word *talent?* Write the word.

_____

COLLABORATE

❸ Talk About It

Why is Diana worried at the end of Scene One? Justify your answer.

_____

_____

_____

ELD.PI.3.1.Ex, ELD.PI.3.1.Br, ELD.PI.3.6.Ex, ELD.PI.3.6.Br, ELD.PI.3.7.Ex, ELD.PI.3.7.Br, ELD.PII.3.6.Ex, ELD.PII.3.6.Br See the California Standards section.

353

Text Evidence

1 Sentence Structure Ⓐ Ⓒ Ⓣ

Look at the third sentence in the messenger's speech. Circle the pronouns. Underline the name that tells who *she* is. Draw a box around the name that the pronoun *you* refers to.

2 Specific Vocabulary Ⓐ Ⓒ Ⓣ

Look at the sentence with the word *boastful*. Someone who is boastful is proud and brags. Why does Athena say that Arachne is boastful?

_____

_____

COLLABORATE

3 Talk About It

Why does Athena decide to have a weaving competition with Arachne? Use text evidence.

_____

_____

⟿ SCENE TWO ⟿

Mount Olympus, home of Athena. A messenger arrives.

MESSENGER: Goddess Athena! I have news from Athens. The weaver Arachne says she can beat you in a weaving competition. She is obsessed with her skill and thinks she is the best weaver in Greece!

ATHENA: I'll show her who weaves the finest cloth! Her obsession with weaving must end. Please get me my cloak. *Messenger hands Athena her cloak.*

ATHENA: Arachne cannot talk about me that way! If she refuses to apologize, I will make her pay for her **boastful** words. Her anguish will be great!

⟿ SCENE THREE ⟿

Arachne's home. There is a knock at the door.

ARACHNE: Who's there?

ATHENA: Just an old woman with a question.

Athena is hiding under her cloak. She enters the room.

ATHENA: Is it true that you **challenged** the goddess Athena to a weaving competition?

ARACHNE: Yes, that's right. *Athena drops her cloak.*

ATHENA: Well, I am Athena. I am here to compete with you!

DIANA: Arachne, please don't! It is unwise to compete with a goddess!

Arachne and Athena sit down at the empty looms and begin to weave furiously.

ELD.PI.3.1.Ex, ELD.PI.3.1.Br, ELD.PI.3.6.Ex, ELD.PI.3.6.Br, ELD.PII.3.2a.Ex, ELD.PII.3.2a.Br
See the California Standards section.

ARACHNE: I am ready to win and get my reward!

ATHENA: There's no prize if you lose!

NARRATOR: Arachne and Athena both wove beautiful cloths. However, Arachne's cloth was filled with pictures of the gods being unkind.

ATHENA: Arachne, your weaving is beautiful, but I am **insulted** and upset by the pictures you chose to weave. You are boastful, and your cloth is mean and unkind. For that, I will punish you.

Athena points dramatically at Arachne. Arachne falls behind her loom and crawls out as a spider.

ATHENA: Arachne, you will spend the rest of your life weaving and living in your own web.

NARRATOR: Arachne was mean and boastful, so Athena turned her into a spider. That's why spiders are now called arachnids. Arachne learned that bragging and too much pride can lead to trouble.

⊷⊷ **THE END** ⊷⊷

Jenny Reynish

Make Connections

? What does Arachne value? How does it cause her trouble? ESSENTIAL QUESTION

What do you value? Why do you value it? TEXT TO SELF

ELD.PI.3.1.Ex, ELD.PI.3.1.Br, ELD.PI.3.6.Ex, ELD.PI.3.6.Br, ELD.PII.3.1.Ex, ELD.PII.3.1.Br, ELD.PII.3.2a.Ex, ELD.PII.3.2a.Br See the California Standards section.

Text Evidence

1 Specific Vocabulary Ⓐ Ⓒ Ⓣ

The word *insult* means to say or do something rude to someone. Why is Athena insulted?

_____

_____

2 Sentence Structure Ⓐ Ⓒ Ⓣ

Reread Athena's last speech. Underline the name of the character who *you* refers to.

3 Comprehension

Theme

Reread the Narrator's last speech. What is the theme of the story that is stated in the speech? What details from the story support the theme?

_____

_____

_____

Respond to the Text

Partner Discussion Work with a partner. Answer the questions. Discuss what you learned about "Athena and Arachne." Write the page numbers where you found text evidence.

How does Arachne feel about her talent for weaving?

Diana tells Arachne that people think _____.

In the drama, Arachne boasts that _____

_____.

Text Evidence 🔍

Page(s): _____

Page(s): _____

Why does Arachne's talent cause her a problem?

I read that Athena is angry because _____.

Arachne challenges Athena to _____.

Arachne's weaving is _____ but Athena thinks it is

_____.

In the drama, Athena turns Arachne into a _____.

Text Evidence 🔍

Page(s): _____

Page(s): _____

Page(s): _____

Page(s): _____

Group Discussion Present your answers to the class. Cite text evidence to justify your thinking. Listen to and discuss the group's opinions about your answers.

ELD.PI.3.1.Ex, ELD.PI.3.1.Br, ELD.PI.3.5.Ex, ELD.PI.3.5.Br, ELD.PI.3.6.Ex, ELD.PI.3.6.Br, ELD.PI.3.9.Ex, ELD.PI.3.9.Br, ELD.PI.3.12.Ex, ELD.PI.3.12.Br

Write Work with a partner. Review your notes about "Athena and Arachne." Then write your answer to the Essential Question. Use text evidence to support your answer. Use vocabulary words from this week's reading in your writing.

Why does Arachne's talent for weaving cause a problem?

First, Arachne boasts _____

_____.

Then, the goddess Athena accepts Arachne's challenge to _____

_____.

Athena and Arachne compete _____

_____.

At the end of the contest, Athena _____

because _____.

Share Writing Present your writing to the class. Discuss their opinions. Think about what the class has to say. Did they justify their claims? Explain why you agree or disagree with their claims. You can say:

I think your idea is _____. I do not agree because _____.

Write to Sources

pages 352–355

Take Notes About the Text I took notes about the play on this chart to answer the question: *Do you think it was fair that Athena turned Arachne into a spider? Give reasons from the text to support your opinion.*

Holly

> Arachne said she was a much better weaver than Athena.

⬇

> Athena came to compete with Arachne.

⬇

> Arachne wove a cloth with mean pictures of the gods.

⬇

> Athena turned Arachne into a spider.

Write About the Text I used my notes to write about Athena turning Arachne into a spider.

Student Model: *Opinion*

I do not think it was fair to turn Arachne into a spider. But Athena was right about Arachne. Arachne was boastful. She told Diana that she was a better weaver than Athena. Athena came to compete with Arachne in a weaving contest. Arachne wove a cloth with mean pictures of the gods. But I do not agree with Athena's action. Changing Arachne into a spider forever is too mean. Now Arachne cannot talk to her friends. She cannot enjoy her life. She is just a spider. This is not a fair way to punish Arachne.

TALK ABOUT IT

Text Evidence
Underline the fourth and fifth sentences. How can you use the word *because* to combine the sentences?

Grammar
Draw a box around the seventh sentence. Add words to describe Athena's action.

Condense Ideas
Circle the sentences that tell what Arachne cannot do. How can you condense the sentences to make one detailed sentence?

Your Turn

Would you like to be a friend of Diana or Arachne? Use reasons from the text to support your opinion.

>> Go Digital
Write your response online. Use your editing checklist.

TALK ABOUT IT

Weekly Concept Weather

? **Essential Question**
How can weather
affect us?

» *Go Digital*

COLLABORATE

What are the kids in the picture doing? How is weather affecting them? Write the words in the web.

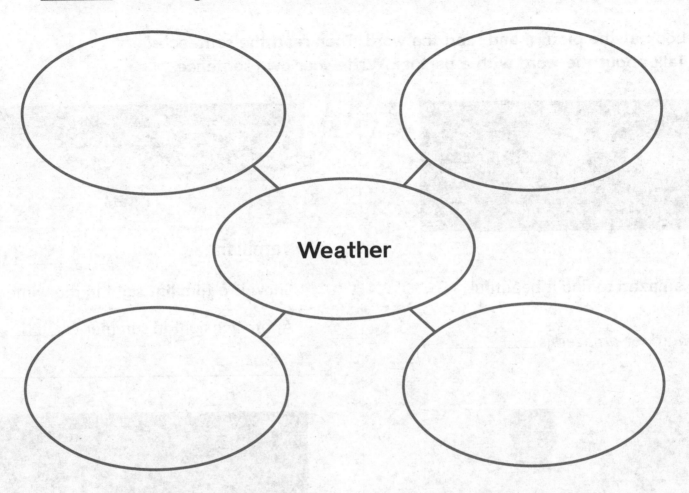

Weather

Discuss what these kids are doing. Discuss how the weather is affecting them. Use the words from the web. You can say:

It is _____ outside today.

The kids are wearing their _____ and _____.

The kids are _____ in the _____.

Ryan McVay/Lifesize/Getty Images

ELD.PI.3.1.Ex, ELD.PI.3.1.Br, ELD.PI.3.6.Ex, ELD.PI.3.6.Br See the California Standards section.

More Vocabulary

COLLABORATE

Look at the picture and read the word. Then read the sentences.
Talk about the word with a partner. Write your own sentence.

amazed

Sam was **amazed** to find a beautiful bird's nest.

Another word for *amazed* is _____.

familiar

Snow is a **familiar** sight in the winter.

A *familiar* sight in summer is _____

_____.

dangerous

Riding a bike without a helmet is **dangerous**.

A word that means the opposite of

dangerous is _____.

huddled

The family **huddled** close to the fire.

I *huddled* under a blanket because _____

_____.

tremendous

The kids raked a **tremendous** amount of leaves.

Another word for *tremendous* is _____.

unable

The cat is **unable** to go inside.

A word that means the opposite of

unable is _____.

Words and Phrases
Phrasal Verbs

stuck at = unable to leave
He is <u>stuck at</u> *home because he is sick.*

stick together = help each other
Best friends will <u>stick together</u> *in high school.*

Read the sentences below. Write the phrasal verb that means the same as the underlined words.

James and his brother always <u>help each other</u>.

James and his brother always _____.

Lee was <u>unable to leave</u> school until Mom came.

Lee was _____ school until Mom came.

>> Go Digital Add the phrasal verbs to your New Words notebook. Write a sentence to show the meaning of each.

COLLABORATE

❶ Talk About It

Read the title. Discuss what you see. Write your ideas.

What does the title tell you?

_____

_____

_____

Who is in the picture?

_____

_____

_____

_____

Take notes as you read the story.

The Big Blizzard

Essential Question

? How can weather affect us?

Read how a blizzard affects the Hernandez family in New York City.

ELD.PI.3.1.Ex, ELD.PI.3.1.Br, ELD.PI.3.6.Ex, ELD.PI.3.6.Br See the California Standards section.

Rosa and Eddie Hernandez **huddled** close to the radio and listened carefully to the scratchy voice of the news announcer.

"The blizzard of 1947 is the biggest snowstorm in New York City history! **Tremendous** amounts of snow and terrible weather **conditions** caused the city's subway system to shut down yesterday. Parents are even forbidding their children to go outside because it is so **dangerous**. The weather forecast for today predicts that the snow will stop. In the meantime, Mayor O'Dwyer's message to all New Yorkers is this: Help each other in the face of this disaster."

"Oh, Mamá!" whispered Rosa. "Will Papá ever get home from work?"

Mamá gave Rosa a big hug. "He must be stuck at work and **unable** to get home," she said. "He is stranded, but don't worry. The snow is slowing down now, and I'm sure he will make it home soon."

Mamá went into the kitchen to make lunch. She came out carrying her coat and scarf.

"We are out of milk and bread, so I need to try to get to Maria's Market," said Mamá.

Rosa and Eddie jumped up and begged to go with her. Mamá had kept them inside for two days because it was snowing too hard to go out.

"No," said Mamá. "It's too cold."

ELD.PI.3.1.Ex, ELD.PI.3.1.Br, ELD.PI.3.6.Ex, ELD.PI.3.6.Br, ELD.PII.3.6.Ex, ELD.PII.3.6.Br
See the California Standards section.

365

Stacey Schuett

Text Evidence

1 Specific Vocabulary Ⓐ Ⓒ Ⓣ

Look at the word *conditions*. In this case, *conditions* means "what is happening with the weather." What conditions are being described? Underline the words that tell you.

2 Sentence Structure Ⓐ Ⓒ Ⓣ

Underline the connecting word *because* in sentence three of paragraph two. What does the dangerous weather cause parents to do? Underline the sentence part that tells you.

COLLABORATE

3 Talk About It

How do the children feel about going outside after the storm?

Use text evidence in your answer.

_____

_____

_____

1 Specific Vocabulary ACT

Reread the third paragraph. Circle the idiom *stick together*. Underline the words that tell what the idiom means. Why does Mamá want the family to stick close together?

_____

2 Sentence Structure ACT

Reread the last two sentences in the sixth paragraph. Circle the commas. Underline the word that tells about Mrs. Sanchez's job. Circle the name of the place she owns.

COLLABORATE

3 Talk About It

Why is Rosa a good neighbor? Justify your answer.

_____

_____

Rosa and Eddie knew they shouldn't argue with Mamá, but they were tired of being indoors.

"Oh please, take us outside! We can all go to the store together!" said Eddie.

"Okay," said Mamá with a sigh. "But we have to **stick together** and stay close to each other."

Mamá helped Rosa and Eddie bundle up in their uncomfortable, but warm, wool clothes. When they got outside, they were astonished and **amazed** to find a wall of snow several feet high! Luckily, their neighbor Mr. Colón arrived with two metal shovels.

"Who wants to help dig out?" he asked.

Mamá, Rosa, and Eddie took turns shoveling snow. It was hard work, but no one fussed or complained. When they were done, they looked across the street. Maria's Market was still snowed in. Mrs. Sanchez, the owner, was trying to clear the snow with a small broom.

"Mr. Colón, may we borrow your shovels, *por favor*?" asked Rosa. "I think we need to give Mrs. Sanchez a hand."

ELD.PI.3.1.Ex, ELD.PI.3.1.Br, ELD.PI.3.6.Ex, ELD.PI.3.6.Br See the California Standards section.

Shoveling the walk in front of the store was easy. It was **a piece of cake** for Rosa and Eddie. They laughed and threw snowballs, too. Mrs. Sanchez was grateful for their help. "*Gracias,*" she said, and gave Mamá milk and bread from her store as thanks.

As Rosa and Eddie crossed the snowy street with Mamá to go home, they heard a deep, **familiar** voice.

"Is that my Rosa and Eddie?"

"Papá!" they shouted and ran over to him. Rosa told him breathlessly about how they helped Mr. Colón and Mrs. Sanchez.

"It is such a relief and a comfort to finally be home," said Papá. "I am so proud of you for helping our neighbors."

Make Connections

? How does the weather affect the Hernandez family? **ESSENTIAL QUESTION**

Tell about a time when you or your family helped out in bad weather. **TEXT TO SELF**

Stacey Schuett

1 Specific Vocabulary A C T

Read the first paragraph. Write the word that means the same as the idiom *a piece of cake*.

_____

2 Sentence Structure A C T

Reread the second paragraph. The word *as* shows that two things are happening at the same time. Circle the word *as*. What two things are happening at the same time?

_____

_____

3 Comprehension
Theme

The theme of a story is the author's message. Think about Mayor O'Dwyer's message. Underline the phrases on this page that support the theme.

ELD.PI.3.1.Ex, ELD.PI.3.1.Br, ELD.PI.3.6.Ex, ELD.PI.3.6.Br, ELD.PII.3.2a.Ex, ELD.PII.3.2a.Br, ELD.PII.3.2b.Ex, ELD.PII.3.2b.Br See the California Standards section.

Respond to the Text

Partner Discussion Work with a partner. Answer the questions. Discuss what you learned about "The Big Blizzard." Write the page numbers where you found text evidence.

How does the big blizzard affect New York City?

I read that Mayor O'Dwyer tells _____.

Page(s): _____

In the story, Papá is stuck _____.

Page(s): _____

Mamá has to go outside _____.

Page(s): _____

In the story, Rosa and Eddie want to _____.

Page(s): _____

Text Evidence 🔍

How do the neighbors help each other?

I read that Mr. Colón _____.

Page(s): _____

In the story Rosa and Eddie help _____.

Page(s): _____

Then Mrs. Sanchez gives _____.

Page(s): _____

Text Evidence 🔍

Group Discussion Present your answers to the class. Cite text evidence to justify your thinking. Listen to and discuss the group's opinions about your answers.

ELD.PI.3.1.Ex, ELD.PI.3.1.Br, ELD.PI.3.5.Ex, ELD.PI.3.5.Br, ELD.PI.3.6.Ex, ELD.PI.3.6.Br, ELD.PI.3.9.Ex, ELD.PI.3.9.Br, ELD.PI.3.12.Ex, ELD.PI.3.12.Br
See the California Standards section.

Write Work with a partner. Review your notes about "The Big Blizzard."
Then write your answer to the Essential Question. Use text evidence to
support your answer. Use vocabulary words from this week in your writing.

How does the weather affect Rosa, Eddie, and Mamá?

First, the weather causes Papá _____.

Then, Rosa, Eddie, and Mamá _____

_____.

Next, Rosa and Eddie help _____.

Mrs. Sanchez gives _____

_____.

Papá is proud of Rosa and Eddie because _____

_____.

Share Writing Present your writing to the class. Discuss their opinions.
Think about what the class has to say. Did they justify their claims? Explain
why you agree or disagree with their claims.

I agree with _____.

That's a good comment, but _____.

Write to Sources

pages 364–367

Harrison

Take Notes About the Text I took notes on this chart to respond to the prompt: *Write a letter from Rosa to her Grandma about the blizzard. Use details from the text.*

> Rosa and Eddie had to stay inside for two days.

> Rosa and Eddie finally got to go out with Mamá.

> Rosa and Eddie helped shovel snow in the neighborhood.

> Papá was stuck at work, but then he came home.

McGraw-Hill Education

370 ELD.PI.3.6.Ex, ELD.PI.3.6.Br See the California Standards section.

Write About the Text I used notes from my chart to write a letter from Rosa to her Grandma.

Student Model: *Narrative Text*

Dear Grandma,

Last week was so exciting! We had to stay inside for two days. There was a blizzard. Papá was stuck at work. So we were worried about him. Then Mamá had to go to the store, so Eddie and I finally got to go out. The snow was higher than my head! Eddie and I helped shovel snow in the neighborhood. And then Papá came home! We were so happy to see him. It was the happiest snow day I have ever had.

Love,

Rosa

TALK ABOUT IT

Text Evidence
Circle the last sentence. Where else does Rosa mention that she was happy or excited? **Underline** those sentences.

Grammar
Underline the word that compares two things in the first sentence about snow. **Circle** the two things being compared.

Connect Ideas
Draw a box around sentence two and three. How can you combine the sentences?

Your Turn

Write a letter from Mamá to her friend Rita. Tell what the family did when they went outside.

>> Go Digital
Write your response online. Use your editing checklist.

ELD.PI.3.1.Ex, ELD.PI.3.1.Br, ELD.PI.3.10a.Ex, ELD.PI.3.10a.Br, ELD.PI.3.10b.Ex, ELD.PI.3.10b.Br, ELD.PI.3.2b.Ex, ELD.PI.3.2b.Br, ELD.PII.3.4.Ex, ELD.PII.3.4.Br, ELD.PII.3.6.Ex, ELD.PII.3.6.Br See the California Standards section.

COLLABORATE

Why is the girl in the picture raising her arms and smiling? How did she reach her goal? Write the words in the web.

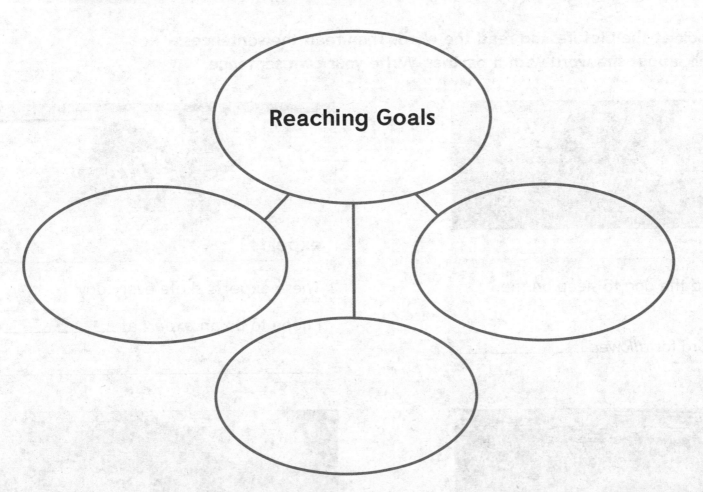

Reaching Goals

Discuss how this girl reached her goal. Discuss how she feels about reaching her goal. Use the words from the web. You can say:

Reaching a goal takes _____.

It also takes a lot of _____ to reach a goal.

She feels _____ about reaching her goal.

ELD.PI.3.1.Ex, ELD.PI.3.1.Br, ELD.PI.3.6.Ex, ELD.PI.3.6.Br See the California Standards section.

More Vocabulary

Look at the picture and read the word. Then read the sentences. Talk about the word with a partner. Write your own sentence.

allowed

We **allowed** the dog to sleep on the couch.

Another word for *allowed* is _____.

attend

Many people **attend** the baseball game.

I *attend* _____

_____.

experts

These **experts** skate every day.

I hope to be an *expert* at _____

_____.

favorite

Her **favorite** animal is the cat.

My *favorite* animal is _____.

honor

It was a great **honor** to meet the mayor.

It would be an *honor* to _____

_____.

responsibility

Taking care of a puppy is a big **responsibility**.

It is my *responsibility* to _____

_____.

Words and Phrases
Phrasal Verbs

came up with = thought of an idea
She came up with a story about a dog and a chicken.

figure out = solve a problem
I will figure out how to fix the bike.

Read the sentences below. Write the phrasal verb that means the same as the underlined words.

Gloria can <u>solve the problem of</u> how to feed everyone.

Gloria can _____ how to feed everyone.

Our teacher <u>thought of an idea for</u> our class song.

Our teacher _____ our class song.

>> Go Digital **Add the phrasal verbs to your New Words notebook. Write a sentence to show the meaning of each.**

Text Evidence

COLLABORATE

1 **Talk About It**

Read the title. Discuss what you see. Write your ideas.

What does the title tell you?

_____

_____

_____

_____

What is this man's job?

_____

_____

_____

_____

_____

Take notes as you read the text.

ROCKETING INTO SPACE

Essential Question

? **Why are goals important?**

Read how one man used his education and experience to reach his goals.

(l) NASA/JPL, (a) Time & Life Pictures/Getty Images

ELD.PI.3.1.Ex, ELD.PI.3.1.Br, ELD.PI.3.6.Ex, ELD.PI.3.6.Br See the California Standards section.

When James A. Lovell, Jr. was a boy, he loved to build rockets and launch them into the sky. But his dreams went a lot farther than his rockets. Like many boys who grew up in the 1930s, Lovell dreamed of being a pilot. And as he watched his rockets **soar**, he knew someday he would, too.

HIGH FLYING DREAMS

Lovell was born in Cleveland, Ohio, in 1928. He worked hard in school and planned to go to a special college to study astronomy and rockets. Unfortunately, he didn't have enough money to **attend**. Lovell had to figure out another way to reach his goal.

Lovell was motivated to find a way to fly rockets. So, he went to college near his home for two years and then signed up for flight training at the United States Naval Academy. After four years at the academy, Lovell joined the United States Navy and became a professional naval test pilot. His job was to fly planes before anyone else was **allowed** to fly them.

James A. Lovell, Jr. became an astronaut in 1962. He flew four space missions.

ELD.PI.3.1.Ex, ELD.PI.3.1.Br, ELD.PI.3.6.Ex, ELD.PI.3.6.Br, ELD.PII.3.2b.Ex, ELD.PII.3.2b.Br
See the California Standards section.

Text Evidence

1 Specific Vocabulary Ⓐ Ⓒ Ⓣ

Reread the last sentence in the first paragraph. *Soar* means "to fly high in the air." What soared into the air?

_____

2 Sentence Structure Ⓐ Ⓒ Ⓣ

Reread the third sentence in the third paragraph. Circle the comma that breaks the sentence into two parts. Box the sentence part that tells when. Underline the two things that Lovell did.

COLLABORATE

3 Talk About It

What steps did Lovell take to become a professional naval test pilot?

1. _____

2. _____

3. _____

Text Evidence

1 Specific Vocabulary ACT

Read the fourth sentence in the first paragraph. What words in the sentence tell what *NASA* means? Underline the words.

2 Sentence Structure ACT

Look at the first sentence in the second paragraph. Circle the phrase that adds a detail about the noun *commander*.

3 Comprehension

Problem and Solution

Reread the third paragraph. Underline the three sentences that tell Apollo 13's problem. Then reread the fourth paragraph. What solution did the experts at NASA find?

_____

_____

_____

PILOT TO ASTRONAUT

As a pilot, Lovell spent more than half of his flying time in jets. He taught other pilots how to fly. He also worked as a specialist in air flight safety. Soon, the National Aeronautics and Space Administration, or **NASA**, put out a call for astronauts. Lovell applied for the job because he had all the essential skills needed to fly into space. As a result, NASA chose him. By 1962, James Lovell was an astronaut! He had finally reached his goal.

BIG CHALLENGES

Lovell flew on three space missions, and then, in April 1970 he became commander of the Apollo 13 mission. This was a big **responsibility** and a great **honor**. This was also one of the biggest challenges of Lovell's life.

Apollo 13 was supposed to land on the Moon. Two days after leaving Earth, however, the spacecraft had a serious problem. One of its oxygen tanks exploded. The crew did not have enough power or air to breathe. They could not make it to the Moon.

Lovell communicated with the **experts** at NASA. No one knew what to do at first. Then the team on the ground did some research and came up with a solution. The astronauts followed the team's directions and built an invention using plastic bags, cardboard, and tape. It worked! It cleaned the air in the spacecraft. But the next problem was even bigger. How were the astronauts going to get back to Earth?

NASA's team works to solve Apollo 13's problem.

ELD.PI.3.1.Ex, ELD.PI.3.1.Br, ELD.PI.3.6.Ex, ELD.PI.3.6.Br, ELD.PI.3.12.Ex, ELD.PI.3.12.Br, ELD.PII.3.1.Ex, ELD.PII.3.1.Br, ELD.PII.3.4.Ex, ELD.PII.3.4.Br See the California Standards section.

A JOB WELL DONE

The NASA team decided the astronauts would use the lunar, or moon, module as a lifeboat. Lovell and the other two astronauts climbed into the smaller spacecraft and shut the hatch tight. They moved away from the main spaceship. With little power, water, food, or heat, the astronauts listened carefully to the team at NASA.

The trip back to Earth was dangerous and scary. For almost four days, the astronauts traveled in the cramped **capsule**. They were cold, thirsty, and hungry. Then, with millions of people watching on television, the module fell to Earth.

Years later, James Lovell said that Apollo 13 taught him how important it was for people to work together. His **favorite** memory was when the capsule splashed down in the Pacific Ocean and he knew they were safe.

A Dream Come True

DID YOU EVER DREAM OF GOING INTO SPACE? CHECK OUT SPACE CAMP!

Space camps have been around for more than 30 years. They make science, math, and technology exciting so kids will want to learn more. And like the NASA training programs, these camps teach the importance of teamwork and leadership.

The Apollo 13 crew splashed down safely on April 17, 1970.

(bkgd) NASA; (i) ©Bettmann/Corbis

Make Connections

? How did Lovell's goals as a child help him as an adult? **ESSENTIAL QUESTION**

Tell about one of your goals and how you can achieve it. **TEXT TO SELF**

Text Evidence

1 Sentence Structure Ⓐ Ⓒ Ⓣ

Look at the second sentence in the first paragraph. Circle the word that connects the two actions. Underline each action.

2 Specific Vocabulary Ⓐ Ⓒ Ⓣ

Reread the second paragraph. A *capsule* is the part of a spacecraft that holds the crew. What word in the paragraph means almost the same as *capsule*? Circle the word.

COLLABORATE

3 Talk About It

Discuss why James Lovell believes that people need to work together. Write your evidence from the text.

_____

_____

_____

_____

ELD.PI.3.1.Ex, ELD.PI.3.1.Br, ELD.PI.3.6.Ex, ELD.PI.3.6.Br, ELD.PI.3.12.Ex, ELD.PI.3.12.Br, ELD.PII.3.6.Ex, ELD.PII.3.6.Br See the California Standards section.

Respond to the Text

Partner Discussion Work with a partner. Answer the questions. Discuss what you learned about "Rocketing Into Space." Write the page numbers where you found text evidence.

What goal did James A. Lovell, Jr. have when he was young?

Text Evidence 🔍

In the text, Lovell dreamed of _____.

Page(s): _____

Lovell wanted to study _____, but _____.

Page(s): _____

I read that that Lovell signed up for _____.

Page(s): _____

How did James A. Lovell, Jr. achieve his goal?

Text Evidence 🔍

According to the author, Lovell taught _____.

Page(s): _____

The text says that in 1962, NASA _____.

Page(s): _____

In April 1970, Lovell became _____.

Page(s): _____

Group Discussion Present your answers to the class. Cite text evidence to justify your thinking. Listen to and discuss the group's opinions about your answers.

380 See the California Standards section.

ELD.PI.3.1.Ex, ELD.PI.3.1.Br, ELD.PI.3.5.Ex, ELD.PI.3.5.Br, ELD.PI.3.6.Ex, ELD.PI.3.6.Br, ELD.PI.3.9.Ex, ELD.PI.3.9.Br, ELD.PI.3.12.Ex, ELD.PI.3.12.Br

Write Work with a partner. Review your notes about "Rocketing Into Space." Then write your answer to the Essential Question. Use text evidence to support your answer. Use vocabulary words from this week's reading in your writing.

Why were goals important for James A. Lovell, Jr.?

When he was a boy, Lovell decided he wanted to _____

_____.

Lovell didn't have enough money to _____ so he _____.

Then Lovell joined the U.S. Navy to _____

_____.

NASA chose Lovell _____ because _____

_____.

Share Writing Present your writing to the class. Discuss their opinions. Think about what the class has to say. Did they justify their claims? Explain why you agree or disagree with their claims.

I think your idea is _____.

I do not agree because _____.

ELD.PI.3.1.Ex, ELD.PI.3.1.Br, ELD.PI.3.3.Ex, ELD.PI.3.3.Br, ELD.PI.3.5.Ex, ELD.PI.3.5.Br, ELD.PI.3.9.Ex, ELD.PI.3.9.Br, ELD.PI.3.10b.Ex, ELD.PI.3.10b.Br, ELD.PI.3.11.Ex, ELD.PI.3.11.Br, ELD.PI.3.12.Ex, ELD.PI.3.12.Br See the California Standards section.

Write to Sources

pages 376–379

Take Notes About the Text I took notes about the text on this chart to answer the question: *What does the author want readers to understand about working hard? Use text evidence to support your answer.*

Yusuf

> James Lovell wanted to go to a special college to study rockets and astronomy.

↓

> Lovell did not have enough money so he went to college and the Naval Academy.

↓

> After that, he joined the U.S. Navy and became a test pilot.

↓

> He became an astronaut with NASA in 1962.

Write About the Text I used notes from my chart to write about the importance of working hard.

Student Model: *Informative Text*

The author wants readers to understand that working hard can help you reach your goal. James Lovell worked hard for many years. He worked hard to reach his goal. He wanted to study astronomy and rockets at a special college. Lovell didn't have enough money so he found another way. First, he went to college for two years. Next, he went to the Naval Academy for flight training. After that, he joined the U.S. Navy and became a test pilot. Then, in 1962, Lovell joined NASA. He was an astronaut! His hard work helped him reach his goal.

TALK ABOUT IT

COLLABORATE

Text Evidence
Underline the sentences about the Naval Academy and the U.S. Navy. **Circle** the words that show the sequence of events.

Grammar
Circle the sentence about money. What adverb can you add to the sentence to tell how Lovell found another way?

Condense Ideas
Underline the second and third sentences. How can you condense these sentences?

Your Turn
COLLABORATE

What problems did the Apollo 13 mission have? How did James Lovell and the NASA team solve them?

>> Go Digital
Write your response online. Use your editing checklist.

Weekly Concept Animals and You

?

Essential Question

How can learning about animals help you respect them?

>> Go Digital

What is the girl in the picture doing? What kind of animal is she learning about? What is she learning to do? Write the words in the web.

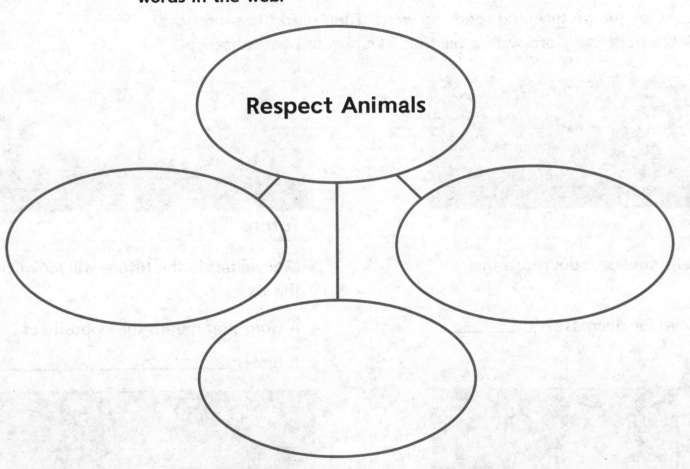

Respect Animals

Discuss how the girl is learning about animals and how she is respecting them. Use the words from the web. You can say:

The girl is learning about an _____.

She is using a _____ to _____ it.

She is learning how to _____ it.

Look at the picture and read the word. Then read the sentences.
Talk about the word with a partner. Write your own sentence.

decrease

The sign tells drivers to **decrease** their speed.

Another word for *decrease* is _____.

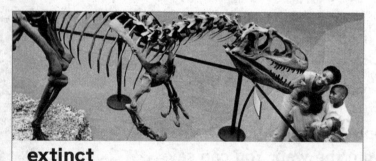

extinct

Dinosaurs are **extinct**.

Some animals become *extinct* because

_____.

future

Many cities in the **future** will look like this city.

A word that means the opposite of

future is _____.

measure

Be sure to **measure** carefully before you cut.

I can use a _____ to *measure* how tall I am.

preserve

National parks **preserve** trees and animals.

Another word for *preserve* is _____.

surroundings

The farm has peaceful **surroundings**.

My *surroundings* at school include _____

_____.

Words and Phrases
Homograph *fall*

fall (*noun*) = **season between summer and winter**
The leaves change color in the <u>fall</u>.

fall (*verb*) = **to drop from a high place to the ground.**
The leaves will <u>fall</u> *to the ground.*

Read the sentences below. Circle the words that mean the same as the underlined words.

The apples will <u>fall</u> onto the ground.

| **season between summer and winter** | **to drop from a high place to the ground** |

Our school year begins in the <u>fall</u>.

| **season between summer and winter** | **to drop from a high place to the ground** |

>> Go Digital Add the homograph *fall* to your New Words notebook. Write a sentence to show each meaning of the word.

COLLABORATE

1 Talk About It

Read the title. Discuss what you see. Write your ideas.

What does the title tell you?

_____

_____

_____

_____

Describe the butterflies you see.

_____

_____

_____

_____

_____

Take notes as you read the text.

Butterflies
Big and Small

(bkgd) Richard Ellis/Contributor/Getty Images News/Getty Images; (r, b) Don Farrall/Photographer's Choice RF/ Getty Images

Essential Question

? How can learning about animals help you respect them?

Read how respecting butterflies can help them survive.

Monarch butterflies like to land in the same trees when they migrate.

ELD.PI.3.1.Ex, ELD.PI.3.1.Br, ELD.PI.3.6.Ex, ELD.PI.3.6.Br See the California Standards section.

There are more than 725 species, or kinds, of butterflies **fluttering** around the United States and Canada. These fascinating creatures taste leaves with their feet and only see the colors red, yellow, and green. The Monarch butterfly and the Western Pygmy Blue butterfly share these same traits, but they are also different in many ways.

SIZE AND COLOR

The Western Pygmy Blue butterfly is the smallest butterfly in the world. It is just about a half-inch across from wing tip to wing tip.

That's smaller than a dime! Monarch butterflies are much bigger. They **measure** about four inches across.

Size is not the only way Monarchs are different from Pygmy Blues. Monarch butterflies are a bright orange color with black markings. That makes them easy to see. Pygmy Blue butterflies are mostly brown and blue, and they blend in with their **surroundings**. Many people walk right by Pygmy Blues, unaware that they are even there.

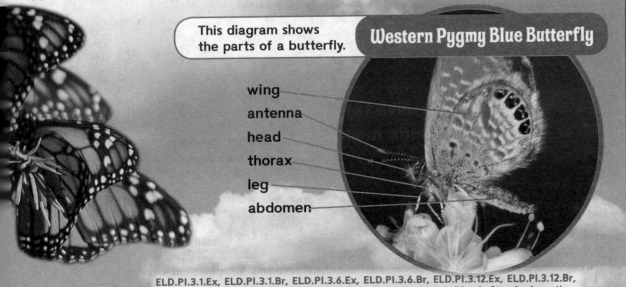

This diagram shows the parts of a butterfly.

Western Pygmy Blue Butterfly

wing
antenna
head
thorax
leg
abdomen

ELD.PI.3.1.Ex, ELD.PI.3.1.Br, ELD.PI.3.6.Ex, ELD.PI.3.6.Br, ELD.PI.3.12.Ex, ELD.PI.3.12.Br, ELD.PII.3.2a.Ex, ELD.PII.3.2a.Br See the California Standards section.

Text Evidence

1 Specific Vocabulary Ⓐ🅒🅣

Reread the first sentence. The word *fluttering* means "moving wings quickly." Where do butterflies in the photograph flutter? Underline the places.

2 Sentence Structure Ⓐ🅒🅣

Read sentence four in the third paragraph. Circle the word that connects the two parts of the sentence. Underline the two pronouns in the second part. What noun do the pronouns refer to? Circle the noun.

3 Comprehension

Compare and Contrast

Read the second and third paragraphs. Write two ways that the Monarch and Pygmy Blue butterflies are different from each other.

_____

_____

389

Text Evidence

1 Sentence Structure Ⓐ Ⓒ Ⓣ

Circle the pronoun *it* where it appears in paragraph one. What noun does *it* refer to? Circle the noun.

2 Comprehension

Compare and Contrast

Reread the first and second paragraphs. How are Monarchs and Pygmy Blues the same? How are they different?

_____

_____

_____

3 Specific Vocabulary Ⓐ Ⓒ Ⓣ

Reread the last sentence in the third paragraph. In this sentence, *journey* is a verb. It means "to take a long trip." What word in this paragraph means almost the same as *journey*? Draw a box around it.

MOVING AROUND

Almost all butterflies migrate, or move to different areas. The Monarch's journey is the longest migration of any butterfly in the world. It spends summers in the northern United States and Canada. Then it migrates south to Mexico in early fall. Many Monarchs travel more than 3,000 miles.

Western Pygmy Blue butterflies inhabit southwestern deserts and marshes from California to Texas. They migrate short distances north to Oregon, and also to Arkansas, and Nebraska.

Both Monarchs and Pygmy Blues migrate. Butterflies are cold-blooded insects. They are hot when the weather is hot and cold when the weather is cold. As a result, Monarch butterflies, which live in areas that get cold during winter, migrate south to stay warm. Western Pygmy Blues **journey** north to find food.

FINDING FOOD

The Western Pygmy Blue drinks the nectar of many kinds of flowers. It finds the sweet, thick liquid easily, so its population has steadily grown. However, Monarch butterflies are not so lucky.

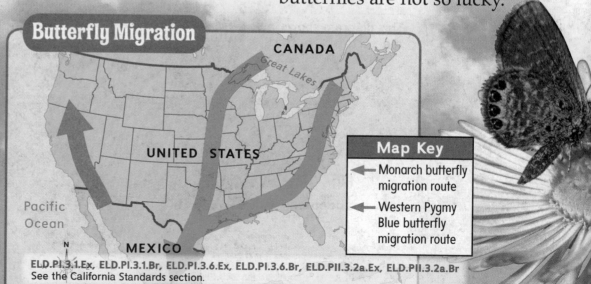

Butterfly Migration

CANADA

Great Lakes

UNITED STATES

Pacific Ocean

MEXICO

Map Key

← Monarch butterfly migration route

← Western Pygmy Blue butterfly migration route

(bkgd) Don Hammond/Design Pics; (b) Mapping Specialists, Ltd.

ELD.PI.3.1.Ex, ELD.PI.3.1.Br, ELD.PI.3.6.Ex, ELD.PI.3.6.Br, ELD.PII.3.2a.Ex, ELD.PII.3.2a.Br
See the California Standards section.

Just like the Pygmy Blue, Monarch butterflies sip nectar from flowers. But the Monarch butterfly has one main food requirement — the milkweed. Monarch butterflies must find this plant along their migration route. But what happens if there are no milkweed leaves?

When people build houses and roads, there are fewer places for Monarchs to find milkweed. If the Monarch cannot find food, its population will **decrease**. The Western Pygmy Blue and Monarch butterflies are not endangered, or **at risk** of becoming **extinct** now, but biologists are worried.

Many other butterflies are endangered because people destroy their habitats.

HELP BUTTERFLIES

Like all wildlife, Monarch and Pygmy Blue butterflies should be respected. People need to **preserve** butterfly habitats. To help, they can work to change laws, plant milkweed, and make it illegal to destroy animal habitats.

Learning about butterflies and what they need to survive is important. That way there will be plenty of Western Pygmy Blue and Monarch butterflies for **future** generations to enjoy.

Monarch butterflies feed on milkweed.

This Western Pygmy Blue butterfly stops to eat.

Make Connections

? How can people learn to respect butterflies? **ESSENTIAL QUESTION**

Talk about butterflies you've seen. How are they alike and different? **TEXT TO SELF**

ELD.PI.3.1.Ex, ELD.PI.3.1.Br, ELD.PI.3.6.Ex, ELD.PI.3.6.Br, ELD.PII.3.2b.Ex, ELD.PII.3.2b.Br
See the California Standards section.

Text Evidence

1 **Sentence Structure**

Reread sentence one in paragraph two. Circle the comma that separates the two clauses. Underline the clause that tells when.

2 **Specific Vocabulary** ⒶⒸⓉ

Reread the second paragraph. When something is *at risk*, it is in danger. When are butterflies at risk of becoming extinct?

_____

_____

COLLABORATE

3 **Talk About It**

How can people respect butterflies? Find text evidence to support your ideas.

_____

_____

(l) ©Premaphotos/Alamy; (r) Medford Taylor/National Geographic/Getty Images

Respond to the Text

COLLABORATE

Partner Discussion Work with a partner. Answer the questions. Discuss what you learned about "Butterflies Big and Small." Write the page numbers where you found text evidence.

What did you learn about Monarch butterflies?

I read that Monarchs migrate _____.

Monarchs need to sip _____ from _____.

The text says if Monarchs do not find _____, they will _____.

Text Evidence 🔍

Page(s): _____

Page(s): _____

Page(s): _____

How can people respect butterflies?

According to the author, people need to protect _____.

I read that people can plant _____ and change _____.

Text Evidence 🔍

Page(s): _____

Page(s): _____

COLLABORATE

Group Discussion Present your answers to the class. Cite text evidence to justify your thinking. Listen to and discuss the group's opinions about your answers.

COLLABORATE

Write Work with a partner. Review your notes about "Butterflies Big and Small." Then write your answer to the Essential Question. Use text evidence to support your answer. Use vocabulary words from this week's reading in your writing.

How does learning about the Monarch butterfly help you respect it?

Monarchs migrate _____.

Monarchs sip nectar _____.

_____.

To preserve Monarch habitats, people need to _____

_____.

We need to respect these butterflies so that _____

_____.

COLLABORATE

Share Writing Present your writing to the class. Discuss their opinions. Think about what the class has to say. Did they justify their claims? Explain why you agree or disagree with their claims.

I agree with _____.

That's a good comment, but _____.

ELD.PI.3.1.Ex, ELD.PI.3.1.Br, ELD.PI.3.3.Ex, ELD.PI.3.3.Br, ELD.PI.3.5.Ex, ELD.PI.3.5.Br, ELD.PI.3.9.Ex, ELD.PI.3.9.Br, ELD.PI.3.10b.Ex, ELD.PI.3.10b.Br, ELD.PI.3.11.Ex, ELD.PI.3.11.Br, ELD.PI.3.12.Ex, ELD.PI.3.12.Br See the California Standards section.

Write to Sources

Take Notes About the Text I took notes on this idea web to respond to the prompt: *Explain why Monarch butterflies migrate. Use evidence from the text.*

pages 388–391

Collin

Monarchs are cold-blooded insects.

Monarchs get cold when the weather is cold.

Monarch butterflies migrate to stay warm.

Monarchs live in the northern United States and Canada. in the summer.

The weather turns chilly in the early fall.

Write About the Text I used notes to write about why
Monarch butterflies migrate.

Student Model: *Informative Text*

Monarch butterflies migrate to stay
warm. Monarch butterflies are cold-blooded
insects. That means they are hot when the
weather is hot, and cold when it is cold.
During the summer, Monarchs live in the
northern United States and Canada. Early
fall comes. The weather turns chilly. Mexico
is warmer than Canada in the winter. So
the Monarchs fly more than 3,000 miles to
Mexico to stay warm!

TALK ABOUT IT

Text Evidence

Draw a box around the conclusion. How
does this sentence retell Collin's main idea in
different words?

Grammar

Underline the sentence that compares two
things. **Circle** the adjective that compares.
What two things are being compared?

Connect Ideas

Circle the fifth and sixth sentences. How can
you use *and* to combine the sentences?

Your Turn

Compare and contrast the size and
color of Monarch and Pygmy Blue
butterflies. Use details from the text.

>> Go Digital
Write your response online. Use your editing checklist.

ELD.PI.3.1.Ex, ELD.PI.3.1.Br, ELD.PI.3.10a.Ex, ELD.PI.3.10a.Br, ELD.PI.3.10b.Ex, ELD.PI.3.10b.Br, ELD.PII.3.1.Ex, ELD.PII.3.1.Br, ELD.PII.3.4.Ex, ELD.PII.3.4.Br, ELD.PII.3.6.Ex,
ELD.PII.3.6.Br See the California Standards section.

? Essential Question
What makes you laugh?

>> Go Digital

COLLABORATE

Why are these two pink pigs funny? What other kinds of things make you laugh? Write the words in the web.

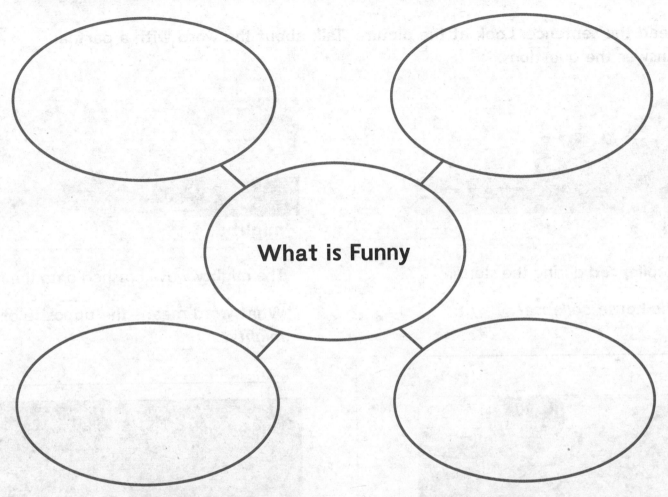

What is Funny

Discuss different things that make you laugh. Use the words from the web. You can say:

My friends laugh when I tell _____ and make _____.

I laugh when things are _____.

My friends and I laugh when we are _____ together.

More Vocabulary

COLLABORATE

Read the sentence. Look at the picture. Talk about the word with a partner. Answer the questions.

collapsed

The house **collapsed** during the storm.

Why did the house *collapse*?

_____

mighty

The **mighty** wave crashed onto the rocks.

What word means the opposite of *mighty*?

_____

inflated

The balloon was **inflated** with hot air.

What other things get *inflated*?

_____

slimy

This slug has **slimy** skin.

What slimy things have you seen?

_____

Poetry Terms

rhyme

The words *moon* and *spoon* **rhyme**.
They end in the same sound.

The astronaut brought a spoon.
On her flight to the Moon.

stanza

A **stanza** is a group of lines in a poem.
This stanza has two lines.

We roughed it at Old Piney Park,
With tents and hot dogs after dark.

(tl)sanapadh/Getty Images; (tr)Evgeny Kuklev/Getty Images; (b)David De Lossy/Getty Images

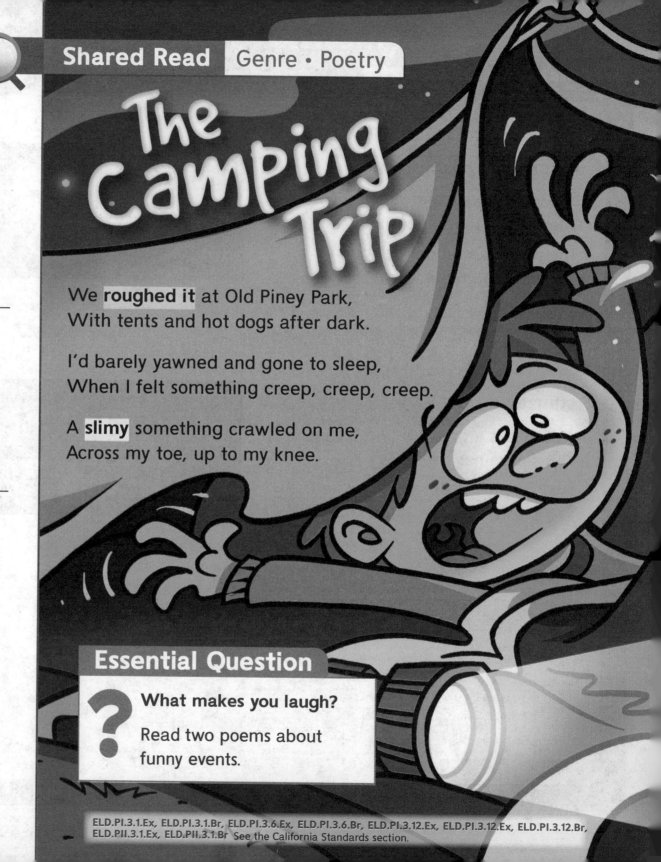

1 Specific Vocabulary ACT

Look at the first line of the poem. The idiom *roughed it* means "camped out in a tent." Where does the narrator rough it?

_____

2 Literary Element Rhyme/Stanza

How many stanzas are on this page?

_____

Underline the rhyming words in each stanza.

3 Sentence Structure ACT

Reread the last stanza. Where does the slimy something crawl? Circle the three places.

The Camping Trip

We **roughed it** at Old Piney Park,
With tents and hot dogs after dark.

I'd barely yawned and gone to sleep,
When I felt something creep, creep, creep.

A **slimy** something crawled on me,
Across my toe, up to my knee.

Essential Question

? **What makes you laugh?**

Read two poems about funny events.

400

ELD.PI.3.1.Ex, ELD.PI.3.1.Br, ELD.PI.3.6.Ex, ELD.PI.3.6.Br, ELD.PI.3.12.Ex, ELD.PI.3.12.Ex, ELD.PI.3.12.Br, ELD.PII.3.1.Ex, ELD.PII.3.1.Br See the California Standards section.

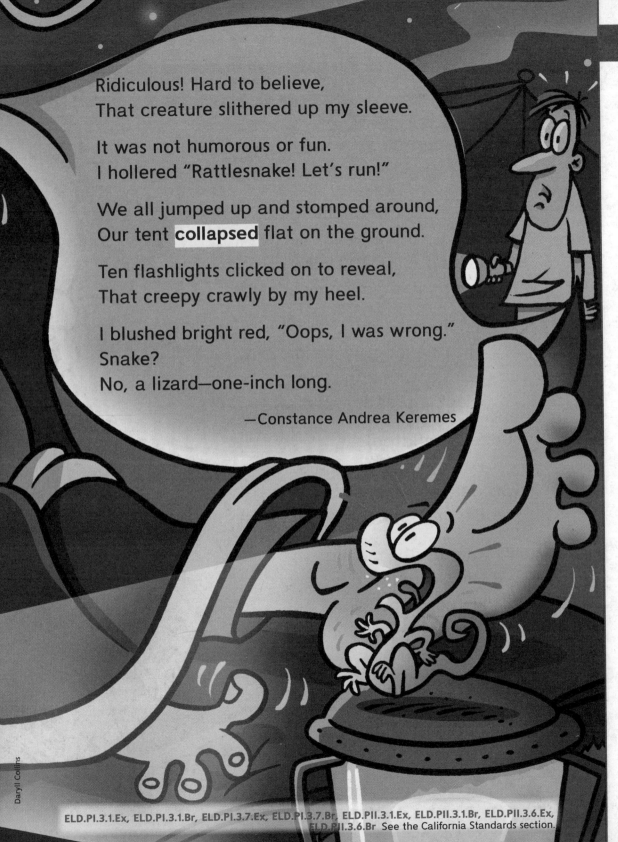

Ridiculous! Hard to believe,
That creature slithered up my sleeve.

It was not humorous or fun.
I hollered "Rattlesnake! Let's run!"

We all jumped up and stomped around,
Our tent **collapsed** flat on the ground.

Ten flashlights clicked on to reveal,
That creepy crawly by my heel.

I blushed bright red, "Oops, I was wrong."
Snake?
No, a lizard—one-inch long.

—Constance Andrea Keremes

**1 Comprehension
Point of View**

What is the narrator's point of view about the creature?

_____

Underline the details that show how the narrator feels.

2 Sentence Structure Ⓐ Ⓒ Ⓣ

Reread the fifth line. Circle the word that connects the two actions. Underline the two actions.

COLLABORATE

3 Talk About It

Reread the last three lines of the poem. Discuss why the speaker blushes. Write the reason.

_____

_____

_____

Daryll Collins

ELD.PI.3.1.Ex, ELD.PI.3.1.Br, ELD.PI.3.7.Ex, ELD.PI.3.7.Br, ELD.PII.3.1.Ex, ELD.PII.3.1.Br, ELD.PII.3.6.Ex, ELD.PII.3.6.Br See the California Standards section.

❶ Literary Element
Rhyme/Stanza

Reread the first stanza of the poem. Circle the words that rhyme. Write the words.

_____

_____

❷ Specific Vocabulary Ⓐ Ⓒ Ⓣ

Reread the second stanza. Look for words that give clues to the meaning of *masticating*. Underline the meaning.

❸ Comprehension
Point of View

Reread the last stanza. How does the father feel about the narrator flying out the door?

_____

_____

Bubble Gum

I bought a pack of bubble gum,
    As I do every week,
Unwrapping 10 or 20 sticks,
    I popped them in my cheek.

I started **masticating**,
    That's a fancy word for chew,
The gum became a juicy gob,
    I took a breath and blew.

I suddenly **inflated**,
    Puffing up like a balloon,
I was a giant bubble,
    Big and round as a full moon.

My father hit the ceiling,
    He was really in a stew,
He hollered, "Stop! Don't go!"
    As out the door I flew.

ELD.PI.3.1.Ex, ELD.PI.3.1.Br, ELD.PI.3.6.Ex, ELD.PI.3.6.Br, ELD.PI.3.8.Ex, ELD.PI.3.8.Br, ELD.PII.3.1.Ex,
ELD.PII.3.1.Br See the California Standards section.

The neighbors' eyes were popping.
　　They **dropped everything** to see.
I was the entertainment of the day.
　　Forget about TV.

If you like bubble gum, beware—
　　Chew just one stick a day,
Or you'll become a bubble, too
And float up　Up　AWAY!

I saw my friends below me,
　　And let loose a **mighty** roar.
WHOOSH!
All my air blew out,
　　And I was just a kid once more.

— Diana Kent

Make Connections

 Which poem made you laugh? Talk about what funny thing happens in each of the poems. **ESSENTIAL QUESTION**

Which poem has the funniest events or characters? **TEXT TO SELF**

Daryll Collins

ELD.PI.3.1.Ex, ELD.PI.3.1.Br, ELD.PI.3.6.Ex, ELD.PI.3.6.Br, ELD.PI.3.11.Ex, ELD.PI.3.11.Br, ELD.PI.3.12.Ex, ELD.PI.3.12.Br, ELD.PI.3.1.Ex, ELD.PII.3.1.Br, ELD.PII.3.2a.Ex, ELD.PII.3.2a.Br
See the California Standards section.

Text Evidence

1 Sentence Structure ⒶⒸⓉ

Reread the first two lines in the first stanza. Circle the pronoun in the second line. What noun does the pronoun refer to? Circle the noun.

2 Specific Vocabulary ⒶⒸⓉ

The idiom *dropped everything* means that people stopped what they were doing. Why did the neighbors drop everything?

_____

COLLABORATE

3 Talk About It

Do you agree with the narrator's advice to the reader to beware? Use text evidence to justify your opinion.

_____

_____

_____

Respond to the Text

Partner Discussion Work with a partner. Answer the questions. Discuss what you learned about "The Camping Trip." Write the page numbers where you found text evidence.

COLLABORATE

What are the funny situations in "The Camping Trip"?

Text Evidence 🔍

Something crawls across the narrator's _____.

Page(s): _____

In the poem, the narrator thinks the creature is a _____.

Page(s): _____

The narrator blushes bright red because _____.

Page(s): _____

What is the funny situation at the end of the poem?

Text Evidence 🔍

I read that the narrator thinks the creature is a _____.

Page(s): _____

In the poem, the flashlights reveal _____.

Page(s): _____

The narrator is wrong because _____.

Page(s): _____

Group Discussion Present your answers to the group. Cite text evidence to justify your thinking. Listen to and discuss the group's opinions about your answers.

COLLABORATE

ELD.PI.3.1.Ex, ELD.PI.3.1.Br, ELD.PI.3.5.Ex, ELD.PI.3.5.Br, ELD.PI.3.6.Ex, ELD.PI.3.6.Br, ELD.PI.3.9.Ex, ELD.PI.3.9.Br, ELD.PI.3.12.Ex, ELD.PI.3.12.Br

Write Work with a partner. Review your notes about "The Camping Trip." Then write your answer to the Essential Question. Use text evidence to support your answer. Use vocabulary words from this week's reading in your writing.

What about this poem made you laugh?

After the narrator goes to sleep, he feels _____

_____.

The narrator hollers _____.

After the campers jump up and stomp around, _____

_____.

The narrator blushes bright red because _____

_____.

Share Writing Present your writing to the class. Discuss their opinions. Think about what the class has to say. Did they justify their claims? Explain why you agree or disagree with their claims.

I agree with _____.

That's a good comment, but _____.

Write to Sources

pages 400–403

Jen

Take Notes About the Text I took notes about the poem on this chart to answer the question: *How does the poet of "Bubble Gum" use rhyme in the stanzas of the poem?*

Stanza	Words that Rhyme

I bought a pack of bubble gum,
    As I do every week,
Unwrapping 10 or 20 sticks,
    I popped them in my cheek.
	week
	
	cheek

My father hit the ceiling,
    He was really in a stew,
He hollered, "Stop! Don't go!"
    As out the door I flew.
	stew
	
	flew

Write About the Text **I used notes to write a paragraph that explains how the poet uses rhyme.**

The poet uses rhyme in each stanza.

A stanza is a group of lines in a poem.

Words that rhyme end in the same sound.

In "Bubble Gum," the stanzas have four lines.

Two of the lines end with words that rhyme.

For example, the author uses the rhyming

words "week" and "cheek." In the last stanza,

the author uses the rhyming words "stew"

and "flew." The poet uses rhymes in two lines

of each stanza.

TALK ABOUT IT

COLLABORATE

Text Evidence

Draw a box around a pair of rhyming words that come from the chart. Why does Jen include these words in her explanation?

Grammar

Circle sentence six. What prepositional phrase can you add to tell where the poet uses the rhyming words *week* and *cheek*?

Connect Ideas

Underline sentences two and three. How can you combine the sentences to connect ideas?

Your Turn

COLLABORATE

How does the poet of "The Camping Trip" use rhyme in the stanzas of the poem?

≫ *Go Digital*
Write your response online. Use your editing checklist.

ELD.PI.3.11a.Ex, ELD.PI.3.11a.Br, ELD.PI.3.10a.Ex, ELD.PI.3.10a.Br, ELD.PI.3.10b.Ex, ELD.PI.3.10b.Br, ELD.PII.3.1.Ex, ELD.PII.3.1.Br, ELD.PII.3.1.Br, ELD.PII.3.5.Ex, ELD.PII.3.5.Br, ELD.PII.3.6.Ex, ELD.PII.3.6.Br See the California Standards section. **407**

California English Language Development Standards

At the bottom of some of the pages in this book, you will see letters and numbers. What do these numbers and letters mean? In **ELD.PI.3.1.Ex**, **ELD** stands for **E**nglish **L**anguage **D**evelopment. The **PI** stands for **P**art **I**. The number **3** stands for Grade 3. The number **1** is the standard number. The **Ex** stands for the language level **Ex**panding.

Part	Grade Level	Standard Number	Level
I	3	1	Expanding

This standard is about speaking in class, small groups, or with a partner to discuss the topic you are learning about during a lesson.

    1. Exchanging information/ideas

This means that you will follow turn-taking rules, ask and answer questions, and add new information to the discussion.

• •

The California English Language Development Standards are divided into three parts:

Part I – Interacting in Meaningful Ways

These standards are about how well you understand spoken English, how you develop and expand your vocabulary, and how well you share information by speaking and writing.

Part II – Learning About How English Works

These standards focus on how well you read, understand, and write different types of texts. This includes understanding how texts are organized, the grammar used in the text, and most importantly, using English to write your own texts to share stories, ideas, and opinions.

Part III – Using Foundational Literacy Skills

These standards are about how well you understand the letters used to form sounds, words, and sentences in English. It is also about how well you use your understanding of letters and sounds to listen, speak, read, and write.

Every standard is presented in three language levels. As you progress through the lessons, you will also progress through each of the language levels. The three language levels are:

Em – Emerging   **Ex** – Expanding   **Br** – Bridging

There may be some standards that you are performing at the third level; there may be other standards where you are performing the basic skills, but most of the standards you may be performing somewhere in the middle.

Your Standards for all three parts and language levels follow. **Take a look!**

Grade 3 California English Language Development Standards

PART I: INTERACTING IN MEANINGFUL WAYS

A. Collaborative

1. Exchanging information and ideas

PI.3.1.Em	Contribute to conversations and express ideas by asking and answering *yes-no* and *wh-* questions and responding using short phrases.
PI.3.1.Ex	Contribute to class, group, and partner discussions, including sustained dialogue, by following turn-taking rules, asking relevant questions, affirming others, and adding relevant information.
PI.3.1.Br	Contribute to class, group, and partner discussions, including sustained dialogue, by following turn-taking rules, asking relevant questions, affirming others, adding relevant information, building on responses, and providing useful feedback.

2. Interacting via written English

PI.3.2.Em	Collaborate with peers on joint writing projects of short informational and literary texts, using technology where appropriate for publishing, graphics, etc.
PI.3.2.Ex	Collaborate with peers on joint writing projects of longer informational and literary texts, using technology where appropriate for publishing, graphics, etc.
PI.3.2.Br	Collaborate with peers on joint writing projects of a variety of longer informational and literary texts, using technology where appropriate for publishing, graphics, etc.

3. Offering opinions

PI.3.3.Em	Offer opinions and negotiate with others in conversations using basic learned phrases (e.g., I think...), as well as open responses in order to gain and/or hold the floor.
PI.3.3.Ex	Offer opinions and negotiate with others in conversations using an expanded set of learned phrases (e.g., *I agree with X, and...*), as well as open responses in order to gain and/or hold the floor, provide counter-arguments, etc.
PI.3.3.Br	Offer opinions and negotiate with others in conversations using a variety of learned phrases (e.g., *That's a good idea, but X*), as well as open responses in order to gain and/or hold the floor, provide counter-arguments, elaborate on an idea, etc.

4. Adapting language choices

PI.3.4.Em	Recognize that language choices (e.g., vocabulary) vary according to social setting (e.g., playground versus classroom) with substantial support from peers or adults.
PI.3.4.Ex	Adjust language choices (e.g., vocabulary, use of dialogue, etc.) according to purpose (e.g., persuading, entertaining), social setting, and audience (e.g., peers versus adults) with moderate support from peers or adults.

Grade 3 California English Language Development Standards

PI.3.4.Br	Adjust language choices according to purpose (e.g., persuading, entertaining), task, and audience (e.g., peer-to-peer versus peer-to-teacher) with light support from peers or adults.
B. Interpretive	
5. Listening actively	
PI.3.5.Em	Demonstrate active listening to read-alouds and oral presentations by asking and answering basic questions with prompting and substantial support.
PI.3.5.Ex	Demonstrate active listening to read-alouds and oral presentations by asking and answering detailed questions with occasional prompting and moderate support.
PI.3.5.Br	Demonstrate active listening to read-alouds and oral presentations by asking and answering detailed questions with minimal prompting and light support.
6. Reading/viewing closely	
PI.3.6.Em	Describe ideas, phenomena (e.g., insect metamorphosis), and text elements (e.g., main idea, characters, setting) based on understanding of a select set of grade-level texts and viewing of multimedia with substantial support.
PI.3.6.Ex	Describe ideas, phenomena (e.g., how cows digest food), and text elements (e.g., main idea, characters, events) in greater detail based on understanding of a variety of grade-level texts and viewing of multimedia with moderate support.
PI.3.6.Br	Describe ideas, phenomena (e.g., volcanic eruptions), and text elements (e.g., central message, character traits, major events) using key details based on understanding of a variety of grade-level texts and viewing of multimedia with light support.
7. Evaluating language choices	
PI.3.7.Em	Describe the language writers or speakers use to support an opinion or present an idea (e.g., by identifying the phrases or words in the text that provide evidence) with prompting and substantial support.
PI.3.7.Ex	Describe the specific language writers or speakers use to present or support an idea (e.g., the specific vocabulary or phrasing used to provide evidence) with prompting and moderate support.
PI.3.7.Br	Describe how well writers or speakers use specific language resources to support an opinion or present an idea (e.g., whether the vocabulary or phrasing used to provide evidence is strong enough) with light support.

Grade 3 California English Language Development Standards

8. Analyzing language choices

PI.3.8.Em	Distinguish how different words produce different effects on the audience (e.g., describing a character as *happy* versus *sad*).
PI.3.8.Ex	Distinguish how different words with similar meanings (e.g., describing a character as *happy* versus *ecstatic*) produce shades of meaning and different effects on the audience.
PI.3.8.Br	Distinguish how multiple different words with similar meanings (e.g., *pleased* versus *happy* versus *ecstatic*, *heard* versus *knew* versus *believed*) produce shades of meaning and different effects on the audience.

C. Productive

9. Presenting

PI.3.9.Em	Plan and deliver very brief oral presentations (e.g., retelling a story, describing an animal, etc.).
PI.3.9.Ex	Plan and deliver brief oral presentations on a variety of topics and content areas (e.g., retelling a story, explaining a science process, etc.).
PI.3.9.Br	Plan and deliver longer oral presentations on a variety of topics and content areas (e.g., retelling a story, explaining a science process or historical event, etc.).

10. Writing

PI.3.10.Em	a) Write short literary and informational texts (e.g., a description of a flashlight) collaboratively (e.g., joint construction of texts with an adult or with peers) and sometimes independently. b) Paraphrase texts and recount experiences using key words from notes or graphic organizers.
PI.3.10.Ex	a) Write longer literary and informational texts (e.g., an explanatory text on how flashlights work) collaboratively (e.g., joint construction of texts with an adult or with peers) and with increasing independence using appropriate text organization. b) Paraphrase texts and recount experiences using complete sentences and key words from notes or graphic organizers.
PI.3.10.Br	a) Write longer and more detailed literary and informational texts (e.g., an explanatory text on how flashlights work) collaboratively (e.g., joint construction of texts with an adult or with peers) and independently using appropriate text organization and growing understanding of register. b) Paraphrase texts and recount experiences using increasingly detailed complete sentences and key words from notes or graphic organizers.

11. Supporting opinions

PI.3.11.Em	Support opinions by providing good reasons and some textual evidence or relevant background knowledge (e.g., referring to textual evidence or knowledge of content).
PI.3.11.Ex	Support opinions by providing good reasons and increasingly detailed textual evidence (e.g., providing examples from the text) or relevant background knowledge about the content.

| PI.3.11.Br | Support opinions or persuade others by providing good reasons and detailed textual evidence (e.g., specific events or graphics from text) or relevant background knowledge about the content. |

12. Selecting language resources

PI.3.12.Em	Use a select number of general academic and domain-specific words to add detail (e.g., adding the word *dangerous* to describe a place, using the word *habitat* when describing animal behavior) while speaking and writing.
PI.3.12.Ex	Use a growing number of general academic and domain-specific words in order to add detail, create an effect (e.g., using the word *suddenly* to signal a change), or create shades of meaning (e.g., *scurry* versus *dash*) while speaking and writing.
PI.3.12.Br	Use a wide variety of general academic and domain-specific words, synonyms, antonyms, and non-literal language to create an effect, precision, and shades of meaning while speaking and writing.

PART II: LEARNING ABOUT HOW ENGLISH WORKS

A. Structuring Cohesive Texts

1. Understanding text structure

PII.3.1.Em	Apply understanding of how different text types are organized to express ideas (e.g., how a story is organized sequentially) to comprehending texts and writing basic texts.
PII.3.1.Ex	Apply understanding of how different text types are organized to express ideas (e.g., how a story is organized sequentially with predictable stages) to comprehending texts and writing texts with increasing cohesion.
PII.3.1.Br	Apply understanding of how different text types are organized to express ideas (e.g., how a story is organized sequentially with predictable stages versus how opinion/arguments are structured logically, grouping related ideas) to comprehending texts and writing cohesive texts.

2. Understanding cohesion

| PII.3.2.Em | a) Apply basic understanding of language resources that refer the reader back or forward in text (e.g., how pronouns refer back to nouns in text) to comprehending texts and writing basic texts.
b) Apply basic understanding of how ideas, events, or reasons are linked throughout a text using everyday connecting words or phrases (e.g., *then, next*) to comprehending texts and writing basic texts. |

Grade 3 California English Language Development Standards

PII.3.2.Ex	a) Apply growing understanding of language resources that refer the reader back or forward in text (e.g., how pronouns refer back to nouns in text) to comprehending texts and writing texts with increasing cohesion. b) Apply growing understanding of how ideas, events, or reasons are linked throughout a text using a variety of connecting words or phrases (e.g., *at the beginning/end, first/next*) to comprehending texts and writing texts with increasing cohesion.
PII.3.2.Br	a) Apply increasing understanding of language resources that refer the reader back or forward in text (e.g., how pronouns or synonyms refer back to nouns in text) to comprehending and writing cohesive texts. b) Apply increasing understanding of how ideas, events, or reasons are linked throughout a text using an increasing variety of connecting and transitional words or phrases (e.g., *for example, afterward, first/next/last*) to comprehending texts and writing cohesive texts.

B. Expanding & Enriching Ideas

3. Using verbs and verb phrases

PII.3.3.Em	Use frequently used verbs, different verb types (e.g., doing, saying, being/having, thinking/feeling), and verb tenses appropriate for the text type and discipline to convey time (e.g., simple past for recounting an experience).
PII.3.3.Ex	Use a growing number of verb types (e.g., doing, saying, being/having, thinking/feeling) and verb tenses appropriate for the text type and discipline to convey time (e.g., simple past for retelling, simple present for a science description).
PII.3.3.Br	Use a variety of verb types (e.g., doing, saying, being/having, thinking/feeling) and verb tenses appropriate for the text type and discipline to convey time (e.g., simple present for a science description, simple future to predict).

4. Using nouns and noun phrases

PII.3.4.Em	Expand noun phrases in simple ways (e.g., adding an adjective to a noun) in order to enrich the meaning of sentences and add details about ideas, people, things, etc.
PII.3.4.Ex	Expand noun phrases in a growing number of ways (e.g., adding comparative/superlative adjectives to nouns) in order to enrich the meaning of sentences and add details about ideas, people, things, etc.
PII.3.4.Br	Expand noun phrases in a variety of ways (e.g., adding comparative/superlative adjectives to noun phrases, simple clause embedding) in order to enrich the meaning of sentences and add details about ideas, people, things, etc.

Grade 3 California English Language Development Standards

5. Modifying to add details

PII.3.5.Em	Expand sentences with adverbials (e.g., adverbs, adverb phrases, prepositional phrases) to provide details (e.g., time, manner, place, cause, etc.) about a familiar activity or process (e.g., They walked *to the soccer field.*).
PII.3.5.Ex	Expand sentences with adverbials (e.g., adverbs, adverb phrases, prepositional phrases) to provide details (e.g., time, manner, place, cause, etc.) about a familiar or new activity or process (e.g., They worked *quietly*; They ran *across the soccer field.*).
PII.3.5.Br	Expand sentences with adverbials (e.g., adverbs, adverb phrases, prepositional phrases) to provide details (e.g., time, manner, place, cause, etc.) about a range of familiar and new activities or processes (e.g., They worked *quietly all night in their room.*).

C. Connecting & Condensing Ideas

6. Connecting ideas

PII.3.6.Em	Combine clauses in a few basic ways to make connections between and join ideas (e.g., creating compound sentences using *and, but, so*).
PII.3.6.Ex	Combine clauses in an increasing variety of ways (e.g., creating compound and complex sentences) to make connections between and join ideas, for example, to express cause/effect (e.g., *The deer ran because the mountain lion came.*) or to make a concession (e.g., *She studied all night even though she wasn't feeling well.*).
PII.3.6.Br	Combine clauses in a wide variety of ways (e.g., creating compound and complex sentences) to make connections between and join ideas, for example, to express cause/effect (e.g., *The deer ran because the mountain lion approached them.*), to make a concession (e.g., *She studied all night even though she wasn't feeling well.*), or to link two ideas that happen at the same time (e.g., *The cubs played while their mother hunted.*).

Grade 3 California English Language Development Standards

7. Condensing ideas	
PII.3.7.Em	Condense clauses in simple ways (e.g., changing: *It's green. It's red. -> It's green and red.*) to create precise and detailed sentences.
PII.3.7.Ex	Condense clauses in a growing number of ways (e.g., through embedded clauses as in, *It's a plant. It's found in the rainforest. -> It's a green and red plant that's found in the tropical rainforest.*) to create precise and detailed sentences.
PII.3.7.Br	Condense clauses in a variety of ways (e.g., through embedded clauses and other condensing as in, *It's a plant. It's green and red. It's found in the tropical rainforest. -> It's a green and red plant that's found in the tropical rainforest.*) to create precise and detailed sentences.

Part III: Using Foundational Literacy Skills

Foundational Literacy Skills (See Appendix A-Grade Three):

	Literacy in an Alphabetic Writing System • Print concepts • Phonological awareness • Phonics & word recognition • Fluency